ELECTR(

MOTORS

Their History, Types, and Principles of Operation

Oleg D. Jefimenko

Professor, West Virginia University

With many illustrations of which 57 are by

David K. Walker

Waynesburg College

Edited by Thomas Valone, PhD, PE

Electrostatic Motors: Their History, Types, and
Principles of Operation

Oleg D. Jefimenko

Copyright © 1973
Originally published by
Electret Scientific Company
Star City, WV

1st Edition - 2011

Reprinted with permission from author by

Integrity Research Institute
5020 Sunnyside Avenue, Suite 209
Beltsville MD 10705
301-220-0440
www.IntegrityResearchInstitute.org

ISBN 978-1-935023-47-0

This book is dedicated to an accomplished farmer,
craftsman, musician, educator, and lawyer
MY FATHER

Table of Contents

FOREWORD

Special thanks to Integrity Research Institute for reprinting this classic work, "Electrostatic Motors, their history, types and principles of operation" by Professor Oleg D. Jefimenko (1973). Oleg was intrigued by IRI's presentations on electrokinetics and electrogravitics and was pleased their mutual interests eventually led to this book.

Professor Jefimenko (1922-2009) was hard-working, gifted, and lucky. He was born in the Ukraine. Caught in the buildup to World War II, he was forced into the Russian army and sent to Siberia for training. He was wounded at the Russian-German front, avoided capture and received medical treatment from a witch-doctor in a nearby village. Later he was apprehended and sent to a German work camp. His independent spirit attracted attention and extra beatings from guards. He managed to trade food rations with another prisoner for a book written in Russian about how to speak German. Guards stopped beating him once he began to speak their language. He improved his situation by learning to run a metal lathe and spent the rest of his time in the camp machining gun barrels.

After the war he studied physics at the University of Goettingen, Germany (Vordiplom, 1950) where he attended lectures of famous scientists of those times. He married and came to the United States in search of new opportunity. His formal education was completed at Lewis and Clark College, Portland Oregon (BA, 1952), and University of Oregon (MA, 1954 and PhD, 1956).

Oleg spent his entire career at West Virginia University Department of Physics. His lectures were enlivened by lecture room demonstrations. Most novel was his water stream "loop-the-loop". Oleg's serious research work involved both theory and experimental aspects of spectroscopy, electricity and magnetism, and electrostatics. After retirement he had more time to explore new topics and wrote books on gravitation - cogravitational fields, electromagnetic retardation, and relativity.

David K. Walker

PREFACE (from original book)

The fascinating science of electrostatics was developed mainly in the 18th century at a time when the technology and industry were too primitive to put this science to practical uses. As a result, serious research in electrostatics soon lost its momentum and, except for a few isolated efforts, was practically nonexistent during the entire 19th century. Only very recently practical aspects of electrostatics began to make their impact on the industry and economy, and the once glamorous but long forgotten science has again appeared at the focal point of serious scientific investigations.

A peculiar obstacle stands, however, in the way of many such investigations: because of the one and one half century of neglect of electrostatic explorations there is a singular lack of easily available quantitative and qualitative information on even the most basic electrostatic phenomena, techniques, and devices. Whereas experimental and theoretical data pertaining to most modern sciences are well documented and are easily retrievable from numerous reference sources, many data in the field of electrostatics must be extracted through thorough and laborious firsthand studies of old books and magazines, the very existence of which is not generally known, and which are not readily available in any of the present-day libraries or repositories.

It is precisely this kind of obstacle that the author encountered, when several years ago he started his research on electrostatic motors. Luckily, however, the obstacle soon transformed itself into a highly rewarding experience of studying various "ancient" books and periodicals and searching through electrostatic inventories of various European and American science museums. In the course of these studies he found numerous forgotten publications on electrostatic motors and found that several old electrostatic motors can actually be seen in some of the museums. (It is interesting to note that the latter motors are usually not on public display, apparently because of a lack of adequate information about their purpose and mode of operation available to museum personnel. It is also interesting to note that certain types of electrostatic motors were frequently employed in various animated toys during the second half of the 18th century, and that, although some of these toys are shown in museums, they are usually shown without an explanation of what made them move or how they were supposed to function.) The purpose of this book is to describe the various types of electrostatic motors reported in the scientific literature between 1700 and the present, and to discuss in general terms their various design features and principles of operation. The book is written for a wide circle of readers, and care has been taken to avoid technical details that would be useful only to a small group of specialists. The readers interested in additional scientific and technical data on the various motors are referred to appropriate original publications cited in this book.

The material is presented in several chapters, each chapter describing a particular class of motors. The sequence of the chapters corresponds to the chronological order in which the earliest motor belonging to each particular chapter was invented. The sequence of material in each chapter is normally arranged also in a chronological order. The last chapter describes some of the most recent research results on electrostatic motors and extrapolates these results into the immediate future.

The author is grateful to his wife Valentina for typing the manuscript and for otherwise helping him to make the book ready for publication. He is also grateful to Dr. David K. Walker for reading the manuscript and for drawing the illustrations for the book.

Oleg D. Jefimenko

Chapter 1   WHAT ARE ELECTROSTATIC MOTORS?

Conventional electric motors create mechanical motion as a result of magnetic forces acting upon electric currents. These motors are properly called *electromagnetic motors.* There is, however, another type of electric motor, in which the motion is created as a result of electric, or "electrostatic", forces acting between electric charges. Motors of this type are called *electrostatic motors.* It is interesting to note that in nature the electrostatic forces are much stronger than the magnetic ones. There are many ways in which this can be demonstrated. For example, although a considerable effort may be needed to separate a magnet from an object attracted by it, a much greater effort is needed to break the magnet; this is because the magnet and the object are held together by magnetic forces, while the molecules of matter in the magnet (as well as in any other body) are held together by electro-static forces.

Why, then, do we not use the electrostatic forces in our electric devices, and in motors in particular, at least on as wide a scale as we use the "inferior" magnetic forces? There are two main reasons for that. First, it is difficult to establish appreciable concentrations of electric charges without causing an electric breakdown in the medium surrounding or supporting the charges (although with modern insulating materials and techniques this difficulty becomes progressively less serious). Second, powerful electrostatic devices require voltages of many kilovolts for their operation, and until recently such voltages could not be produced conveniently and economically. Motors of great power, however, are not the only ones needed. Equally important are low power motors capable of performing various special tasks. In this respect electrostatic motors may compete successfully with their electromagnetic cousins even now.

Although electrostatic motors are not yet widely known or used, they already hold at least five very impressive records as compared with the electromagnetic motors:

1. The first electric motor ever invented was an electrostatic one. It was built about 100 years before the first electromagnetic motor was conceived

2. The electric motor that operated without interruption longer than any other electric motor was an electrostatic one. This was a pendulum type motor, known as the "electric perpetuum mobile", installed at the University of Insbruck, Austria, in 1823. Since then it operated continuously at least until 1909, powered by a Zamboni pile (an early high-voltage battery).

3. Electrostatic motors have been operated from voltages in excess of 10^5 volts (100 kV), which is much higher than the voltages suitable for operating electromagnetic motors.

4. Electrostatic motors have been operated by using currents smaller than 10^{-9} amps, which is much less than the currents needed to operate electromagnetic motors.[*]

5. The first electric motor that operated directly from the atmospheric electricity was an electrostatic motor. None of the presently available electromagnetic motors can operate directly from this source.

Even this short list reflecting some of the more obvious peculiarities of electrostatic motors shows quite clearly that electrostatic motors possess a number of unique properties. These properties undoubtedly will make electrostatic motors increasingly more important for the science, engineering, and technology of the future. Many different types and designs of electrostatic motors are possible. It is customary to classify electrostatic motors in accordance with some prominent feature of their mode of operation or some prominent feature of their design. Thus, in reference to the techniques used for delivering electric charges to the active part of a motor one speaks of *contact motors, spark motors, corona motors, induction motors,* and *electret motors.* In reference to the medium in which the active part of a motor is located one speaks of

---

[*] This amount of current is equal to <u>one nanoampere</u>, which is one millionth of a milliamp. It is still today an incredibly low amount of electric charge flow per second, proving that electrostatic motors only need voltage to work. – Ed. note

liquid- or gas-immersed motors. In reference to the material and design of the active part of a motor one speaks of *dielectric motors* (the active part is made mainly of dielectric material) and *conducting-plate, or capacitor, motors* (the active part is made mainly of metal and resembles a variable capacitor). Finally, in reference to the rate of rotation of a motor relative to the period of the applied voltage (for ac operated motors) one speaks of *synchronous motors* and *asynchronous motors.* This classification of electrostatic motors does not make it possible, however, to specify uniquely each individual motor. Also, two or more different operation modes are usually possible for most electrostatic motors (for example, certain motors can be operated at will as contact, spark, or corona motors). Therefore an assignment of a particular motor to one or another of the above types or categories is frequently more or less arbitrary. This applies, of course, also to the present book, where certain motors described in the chapters that follow could be equally well discussed under different chapter headings, and where the inclusion of certain motors in a particular chapter was occasionally dictated by the fact that such an inclusion resulted in a more coherent development of the subject matter.

PLATE 1

Here is what H.B. Dailey wrote about this electrostatic motor which he and his father built in 1880: *"Whether or not there is about the instrument and its history that which would ever give it a claim to any measure or serious interest, it is at least an electric motor most unique. A motor without magnetism, wiring, or any iron in its make up. A motor that runs by the action of the direct push and pull of the pure unconverted electricity itself."*

PLATE 2

It was Benjamin Franklin who in 1748 constructed the first electrostatic motors. No original drawings or models of his motors are known to exist, but his first motor must have looked very similar to this replica designed by the author for the Electret Scientific Company.

PLATE 3

Franklin's second motor probably looked very much this replica also designed by the author for the Electret Scientific Company. Whereas the first motor operated from the electricity stored in Leyden jars, this motor operated from the electricity stored in the motor itself.

PLATE 4

The first corona motor was designed around 1869 by the German physicist Poggendorff. Pogendorff made a thorough study of the motor, but failed to appreciate its possibilities in the mistaken belief that no sources of electricity could supply enough power to any electric motor to make it do useful work. This simplified version of Poggendorff's motor was built by the author.

PLATE 5

The electret—a permanently electrized dielectric-is essentially a product of the 20th century. When an electret is placed between slotted electrodes to which a voltage is applied, the electret experiences a force. This motor designed by the author utilizes the slot effect. The rotor of the motor is a carnauba wax electret made of two oppositely polarized half-disks. The motor was built in 1966.

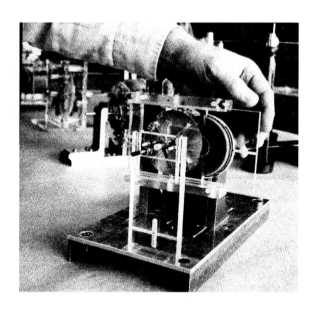

PLATE 6

A more practical design of an electret motor in-
corporates stationary electrets and rotating electrodes.
The electrets can be easily withdrawn from the motor for
servicing or replacement. The motor operates from
approximately 60 volts dc. This particular motor was the
first ever operated from atmospheric electricity.

PLATE 7

In this electret motor developed in the author's laboratory (as were all the electret motors reproduced in these photographs) several thin mica electrets are used as active elements. This arrangement of electrets makes good use of the available space and allows one to construct relatively powerful electret motors.

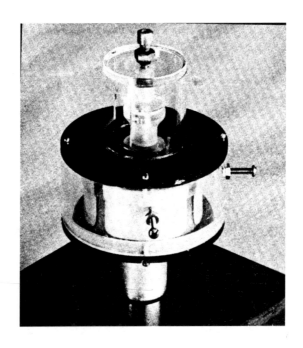

PLATE 8

This "hoop" electret motor built in 1967 by D. K. Walker has a stationary cylindrical electret. The rotor is made of four pairs of bent aluminum plates enclosing the electret. The motor requires no commutator. The motor has been operated for several years without any servicing.

PLATE 9

Corona motors are probably the most promising electrostatic motors. This 0.1-hp modern version of the Poggendorff motor has a cylindrical rotor instead of a disk. The motor operates from a 6000-volt power supply as well as from an earth field antenna.

PLATE 10

The operation of electrostatic motors from antennas can
be demonstrated with this lecture room apparatus. The
Van de Graaff generator produces electric charges in the
air. The sharp point antenna collects the charges from
the air and delivers them to one terminal of an electrostatic motor whose other terminal is grounded.

PLATE 11

The author and D. K. Walker attempt to operate an electret motor from a 20-foot pole antenna in front of the Physics Building of the West Virginia University. The tall building screened the atmospheric field, and the motor did not run, although it operated very well from the same antenna in the nearby unobstructed parking lot.

PLATE 12

The author operates electrostatic motors by means of an airborne antenna.

Chapter 2   ELECTRIC PENDULUM MOTORS; CONTACT MOTORS

If "electric motor" is understood to be a device converting electric energy into a continuous mechanical motion, then the first two electric motors were invented in the early 1740's by Andrew Gordon, a Scottish Benedictine monk and professor of philosophy at Erfurt, Germany.[1] Gordon's first motor was a device known as the "electric bells" (his second motor will be described in the next chapter). The device and its operation were as follows. A metallic clapper (pendulum) was suspended by a silk thread between two oppositely charged bells (Fig. 1). From an initial contact with one of the bells the clapper acquired a charge of the same polarity as that of the bell. Due to repulsion of like charges and attraction of opposite charges the clapper was then repelled by this bell and attracted by the second bell. As the clapper struck the second bell, it gave off its initial charge and acquired a charge of the same polarity as that of the second bell. Then the clapper was repelled by the latter and attracted by the first bell, which it struck again, and so on. Numerous variations of Gordon's bells have been described by later authors, mostly as devices for lecture-room demonstrations of electrostatic forces. Such devices are widely used for this purpose even now.

An ingenious application of Gordon's bells was made by Benjamin Franklin in 1752. He connected the bells to an insulated lightning rod as a warning device "to give notice when the rod should be electrified."[2] (It appears that at that time neither Franklin nor any other scientist suspected how dangerous this "warning" device could be. The extreme danger of experiments with insulated lightning rods became clear a year later, when in 1753 the Russian physicist George Wilhelm Richmann was killed by lightning that entered his laboratory through such a rod, as he approached it in order to measure its electrification with a specially constructed electrometer.) In a later modification of Gordon's invention one of the two bells was mounted on a Leyden jar (Fig. 2); the bells would then ring for as long as there was enough electric energy stored in the jar to move the clapper. (Franklin described the operation of an electric pendulum powered by a Leyden jar in 1747; see Ref. 2, p. 189.)

Sometimes Gordon's bells were made as a set of three bells and two clappers, all suspended from a horizontal bar, the central bell being insulated from the bar and grounded by means of a light chain (Fig. 3).

Another modification of Gordon's bells was a set of bell chimes arranged in a circular formation around the central bell (Fig. 4); a separate clapper was then present for each of the outside bells, each clapper moving between one of the latter and the central bell (the central bell was usually grounded, the outside bells were connected to an electrostatic generator). The electrical and mechanical principle of Gordon's invention could be used, of course, not only for ringing bells but also for a variety of other purposes. In particular, this principle was later used in two electrically operated toys: the "electric swing" and the "electric seesaw", which utilized, respectively, an insulated pendulum made as a swing (Fig. 5) and an insulated conducting swing bar capable of oscillating about a horizontal axis (Fig. 6).[3,4]

Except for Franklin's bells, all of the above devices were designed for operation from an electrostatic generator or from Leyden jars charged by such a generator. However, in 1806 a high-voltage chemical battery ("dry pile", later known as the "Zamboni pile") was invented by Georg Behrens, and in 1810 this pile was adapted by Giuseppe Zamboni to operate primitive electrostatic motors.[5] Inasmuch as a Zamboni pile could remain active for many years, the little motors that operated from it were known as the "electric perpetuum mobile". An example of such a perpetuum mobile is shown in Fig. 7 (see Chapter 4 for another design). The apparatus consisted of a light rigid insulated pendulum, pivoted just above the center of gravity, with a light conducting ring at the top. The ring was located between the two knobs of a Zamboni pile. When the ring contacted one of the knobs, it acquired a charge from the knob and was repelled from this knob and attracted to the second knob, and so on, just like the clapper in Gordon's bells. One such perpetuum mobile is reported to have operated without interruption for at least 86 years.[6] The most sophisticated device derivable from Gordon's electric bells was probably the reciprocating electrostatic motor (Fig. 8 and Plate 1) built in 1880 by Howard B. Dailey and Elijah M. Dailey.[7]

The motor, which is now at the Museum of History and Technology of the Smithsonian Institution, was described by one of its builders as follows: "This machine operates by the direct action of static electric attractions and repulsions. It is constructed entirely of fine wood, glass and hard rubber, there being no magnetic materials used. The flywheel is of laminated, soft wood and runs in journal bearings of very small diameter. The moving balls, mounted on the walking beam of vulcanite, are made of wood, hollowed out so that the walls are about 2 millimeters thick. They are covered with aluminum foil for static conductivity. The stationary balls are of solid wood. To operate the engine the stationary balls are charged with electricity form a static electric generator, such as a Holtz machine, the upper balls being connected through the brass ball to one pole of the machine while the lower stationary balls are connected through the binding post on the bed frame to the opposite pole of the machine. Under proper conditions when charged, the engine will make about 375 revolutions per minute. The walnut base upon which the engine is mounted is 14" long, 4" wide and 1¾" thick. The movable balls are about 1½" in diameter; the upper stationary balls are 1¾" in diameter; and the lower stationary balls, 1½". The four glass rods, mounted vertically, are about 6" high and spaced 6" apart along the bed. The diameter of the flywheel is 5¾". It is gilded and has wire spokes and the connecting rod is 7" in length.

The electric principle of Gordon's bells can be used also for producing a continuous unidirectional motion. A fascinating device of this type was the "electric racing ball" of the "electric planetarium" with an excellent description provided by M. Guyot.[8] The apparatus consisted of an insulated horizontal conducting hoop positioned above a conducting disk having a vertical rim concentric with the hoop (Fig. 9).

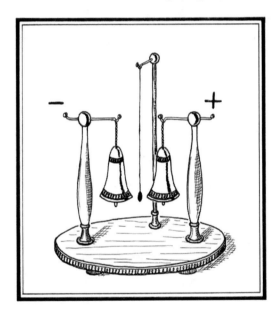

Figure I

The so-called "electric bells" constituted the first device that converted electrical energy into a continuous mechanical motion. They were invented in about 1742 by Andrew Gordon, a professor of philosophy at Erfurt, Germany.

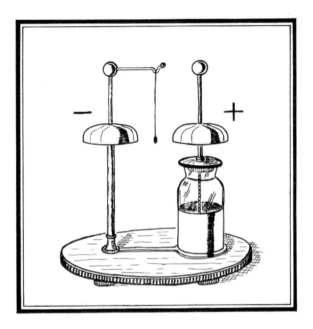

Figure 2

In a later modification of Gordon's invention one of the two bells was mounted on a Leyden jar. The bells would then ring for as long as there was enough electrical energy stored in a jar to move the clapper.

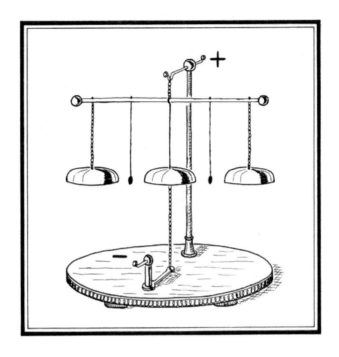

Figure 3

Sometimes Gordon's bells were made as a set of three bells and two clappers, all suspended from a horizontal bar, the central bell being insulated from the bar and grounded by means of a light chain.

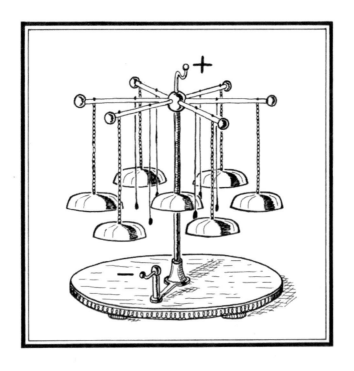

Figure 4

Another modification of Gordon's bells was a set of bell chimes arranged on a wooden base in a circular formation around the central bell. A separate clapper was then present for each of the outside bells.

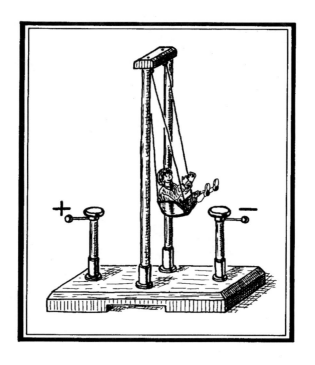

Figure 5

The electrical and mechanical principle of Gordon's invention could be used not only for ringing bells but for creating a mechanical motion in general. In this "electric swing" this principle was used to operate an animated toy.

Figure 6

Various electrostatically operated toys were invented in the 18th and 19th centuries. This "electric seesaw" was basically a conducting bar oscillating about a horizontal axis on the same principle as the clapper of Gordon's bells

The arrangement constituted a track for a light sphere of glass placed on the disk between the hoop and the rim. When the hoop and the disk were connected to an electrostatic generator, the sphere ran along this track due to attraction and repulsion exerted by the hoop and the disk upon the points of the sphere that acquired charges from contact with the disk' and the hoop (the rolling of the sphere usually had to be initiated with a light push by hand, but once the sphere had started to run, it continued running for as long as the electrostatic generator was in operation).

Since the moving elements in the above described motors were charged by contact, the motors may be classified as "contact motors". This method of charging, however, is neither the only possible nor the most expedient one. Therefore contact motors will probably always be subordinate to most of the motors described in the following chapters. In this connection it may be useful to note that, upon a closer examination of the operation of Gordon's bells and other similar devices, one recognizes that the charging of the moving elements in these devices usually occurs by means of a spark that jumps from a stationary electrode (bell) to a moving element (clapper) as soon as the latter comes close enough to the former. Thus the actual physical contact between the moving and stationary components in these devices is not at all necessary for their operation. In fact, such a contact is harmful insofar as it results in energy losses from impact and friction.

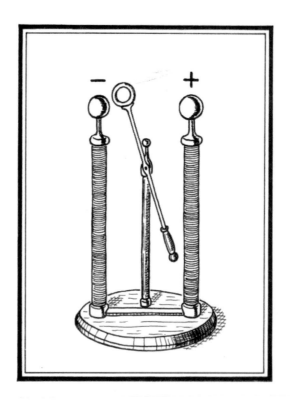

Figure 7

This electric pendulum operated from a Zamboni pile, an early high voltage battery. Since the pile remained active for years, the pendulum was known as an "electric perpetuum mobile".

Figure 8

The most sophisticated device derivable from Gordon's bells was probably this reciprocating electrostatic motor built in 1880 by H. B. Dailey and E. M. Dailey

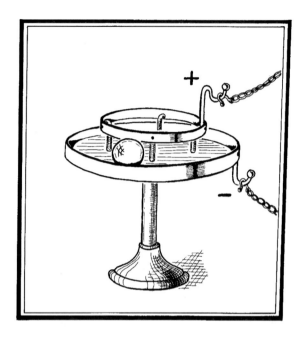

Figure 9

The electric principle of Gordon's bells could be used also for producing a continuous unidirectional motion. This "electric racing ball" was propelled along a conducting hoop by the same mechanism that moved the clapper in Gordon's bells.

REFERENCES

1. P. Benjamin, *A History of Electricity,* John Wiley and Sons, New York, 1898, pp. 506, 507.
2. J. Sparks, Ed., *The Works of Benjamin Franklin,* Whittemore, Niles, and Hall, Boston, 1856, Vol. 5, p. 301.
3. F. M. Avery, *Modern Electricity and Magnetism,* Sheldon and Company, New York, 1885, p. 241.
4. A. Neuburger, *Erqotzliches Experimentierbuch,* Ullstein & Co., Berlin, 1920, pp. 434-436.
5. Gilbert, *Annalen der Physik,* Ser. 1, Vol. 49, pp. 35-46, (1815).
6. Muller-Pouillet, *Lehrbuch der Physik und Meteorologie,* Friedrich Vieweg und Sohn, Braunschweig, 1909, 10th edn., Vol. 4, p. 338.

7. H. B. Dailey, *Modern Electrics* , Vol. 5, pp. 916-917 (1912).
8. M. Guyot, *Nouvelles Recreations Physiques et Mathematiques,* Gueffier, Paris, 1786, Vol. 1, pp. 272-274 and Plate 27.

(The author is grateful to Mr Elliot N Sivowitch, Smithsonian Institution Museum Specialist, for kindly providing this description and the photograph of the Dailey's motor).

Chapter 3 ELECTRIC WIND MOTORS

As already mentioned in the preceding chapter, Andrew Gordon invented two electric motors. His second motor was the "electric fly",[1,2] also known as the "electric whirl", "electric pinwheel", or "electric reaction wheel" (Fig. 10). The electric fly consisted of one or more light metal arms with sharp-point ends bent at right angles to each arm and in the same circumferential direction. The fly was pivoted at its center on an insulated needle. When the needle was connected to an electrostatic generator, a corona discharge* took place from the sharp points of the fly. The air near these points became charged with charges of the same polarity as that of the fly and was then repelled from the points due to repulsion of like charges (the resulting motion of the air is known as the "electric wind"). Similarly, the points themselves were repelled from the charges in the air, and the fly rotated therefore in the opposite sense to that in which the points were directed.

Also the electric fly was used for ringing bells or chimes. This was accomplished by suspending from the fly a clapper, which, as the fly rotated,

*Corona discharge is a spontaneous electric conduction in a gas (air) originating from sharp conducting bodies whose electrostatic potential relative to the ground is 3000 volts or higher.

struck in turn several bells positioned in a circular formation underneath the fly (Fig. 11).[3]

In 1760, Hamilton, professor of philosophy at Dublin, suggested to use a similar device as an electrometer.[4] In this electrometer small weights were suspended from the fly. As the fly turned, the weights were deflected from the vertical direction by centrifugal forces. This deflection was a measure of the fly's speed and, hence, of the strength of the source to which the fly was connected. A more sophisticated electrometer utilizing the electric fly was described by Jakob Langenbucher,[5] a silversmith at Augsburg, Germany, who spent a large part of his time and fortune on improving electrostatic generators and studying electrostatic phenomena. In this electrometer the fly was mounted on a thin vertical cylinder. A fine string was fastened to the cylinder. The string passed over a small pulley and had a light pan attached' to its free end. A small weight was placed on the pan. As the fly turned, the string wound itself on the cylinder lifting the pan and the weight. The maximum weight that could be lifted by this electrometer was a measure of the strength of the source from which the fly was operated.

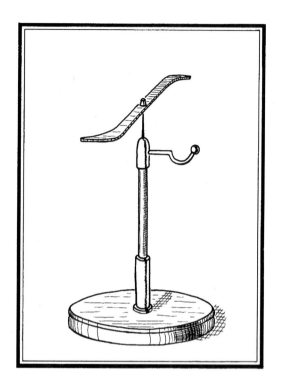

FIGURE 10

Andrew Gordon invented two electric motors. His second motor was the so-called "electric fly".

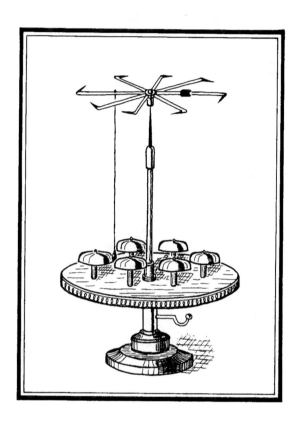

FIGURE 11

Also the electric fly was used for ringing bells with the aid of
a clapper suspended from it.

The principle of the electric fly was later used to operate an orrery depicting the orbital motions of the Sun, the Moon, and the Earth (Fig. 12).[6] In such an orrery, also known as the "electrical tellurium", the longer bent arm carried a large sphere at one end, while at the other end it carried a similar but smaller bent arm, each end of which also carried a small sphere. The three spheres represented the Sun, the Moon, and the Earth. The arms were pivoted on sharp points, and each arm had a perpendicular sharp point in the horizontal plane. When the instrument was connected to an electrostatic generator, the two systems rotated about their points of support, the smaller system, being lighter, rotated more rapidly than the larger one. The relative masses of the spheres were adjusted to make the Earth-Moon system rotate twelve times for every single rotation of the Sun.

An interesting variation of the electric fly was constructed in 1761 by Ebenezer Kinnersley, a Philadelphia school teacher and close friend of Benjamin Franklin. Kinnersley called his device the "electrical horse-race".[7] This was a cross formed by two pieces of wood of equal length (probably about 18 inches long) supported horizontally on a central pin. A light figure of horse with his rider was placed upon each extremity of the cross, The motion was produced by corona discharge from the spurs of the riders (Fig. 13). The electrical horse-race was a popular toy in the latter part of the 18th century. Interesting descriptions of this toy have been provided by Langenbucher (Ref. 5, p. 206 and Plate 8), and by Guyot.[8] To show more convincingly that the electric fly converted electrical energy into mechanical energy, electric flies were placed on horizontal axes and were arranged to lift small weights (Fig. 14) or to climb inclined rails (Fig. 15).[9]

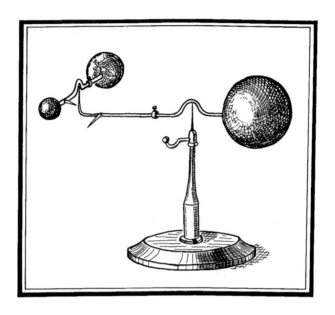

FIGURE 12

The principle of the electric fly was later used to operate an orrery depicting the orbital motions of the Sun, the Moon, and the Earth. The masses of the spheres were adjusted to make the Earth-Moon system rotate twelve times for every single rotation of the Sun.

FIGURE 13

An interesting variation of the electric fly was constructed
in 1761 by Ebenezer Kinnersley, a friend of Benjamin
Franklin. Kinnersley called his device the "electrical horse-
race". The electrical horse-race was a popular toy in the
latter part of the 18th century.

Operation of the electric fly in liquids was investigated by Aime.[10] A historical account of electric fly studies was presented by Tomlinson.[11] The mechanism of the fly was discussed at some length by Mascart.[12] A quantitative study of the forces acting upon the electric fly was performed by Kampfer.[13]

A more efficient modification of the electric fly was proposed in 1887 by Bichat.[14] Bichat's electric "tourniquet" consisted of a light vertical frame capable of turning about a vertical axis and supporting two thin vertical wires producing a corona discharge along their entire length. The vertical sides of the frame acted as "spoilers" preventing a corona discharge from the "back side" of the wires. A simple motor based on Bichat's device is shown in Fig. 16.

In recent years the principle of the electric fly (reaction force experienced by a sharp point as a result of a corona discharge from it) has been suggested for a flying machine ("corona-kraft levitation").[15] The lift realizable from such a machine does not, however, appear to be of practical significance.[16]

Closely related to the electric fly were the "electric wind wheels" and the "electric wind turbines". Like the electric fly, they were invented in the 1740's and utilized a corona discharge from sharp points for their operation. Benjamin Franklin studied these devices in 1747 (he first learned of them from his friend Philip Syng). According to Franklin (Ref. 7, p. 184) they were "light windmill-wheels made of stiff paper vanes; also ... little wheels, of the same matter, but formed like water-wheels". Their probable appearance was as shown in Figs. 17 and 18. Later versions of these devices have been described by Guyot (Ref. 8, pp. 274, 275 and Plate 27), by Langenbucher (Ref. 5, pp. 75, 76 and Plate 3), by Gale,[17] and by Neuburger.[18]

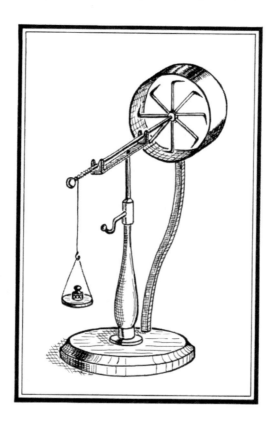

FIGURE 14

Electric fly converted electrical energy into mechanical energy and could lift small weights.

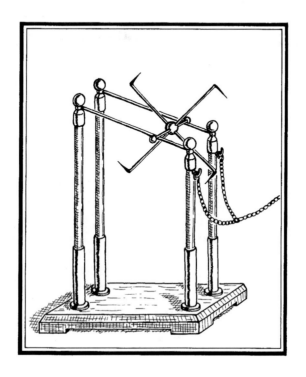

FIGURE 15

Electric fly developed enough mechanical energy for climbing inclined rails.

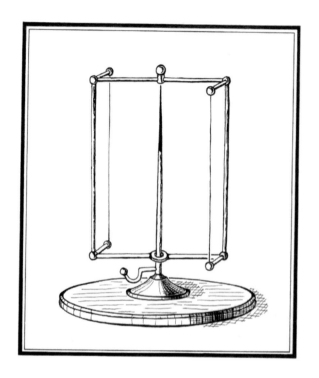

FIGURE 16

A more efficient modification of the electric fly was proposed in 1887 by Bichat, who called his device the "electric tourniquet".

A delightful electric toy using the electric wind for its propulsion was made by W. R. King,[*] an associate of James Wimshurst (the designer of the electrostatic machine carrying his name). This toy, which may be called an "electrical rabbit hunt", now at the Science Museum in London, is shown in a simplified form in Fig. 19. It consists of a small electric wind turbine mounted on a vertical shaft carrying five light metal arms on its upper end; the arms support figurines of a rabbit, three dogs, and a horseman, who chase each other in a beautiful little garden, as the arms turn powered by the turbine below.

In studying the electric wind motors, Benjamin Franklin concluded that their action depended not as much on the electric wind as such, but on the repulsion and attraction of electric charges present on the moving and stationary parts of the motors (Ref. 7, p. 184). It is very probable that this conclusion led him to the invention of his big electric motors, the famous "electrical wheels", which are described in the next chapter.

---

[*] In the caption to Figure 19, the author indicates "E.R. King" as the designer, rather than "W.R. King", one of which is in error. – Ed. note

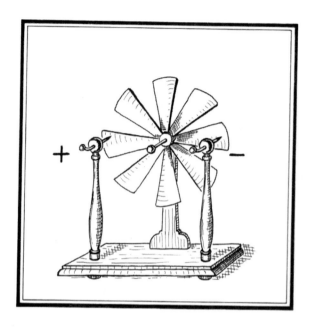

FIGURE 17

Closely related to Gordon's electric fly was the "electric wind wheel". Like the electric fly, it was invented in the 1740's and utilized a corona discharge from two sharp points for its operation.

FIGURE 18

Benjamin Franklin studied this "electric wind turbine" in 1747. He concluded that its action depended not as much on the electric wind as on the forces between the charges present on its moving and stationary parts.

FIGURE 19

A delightful electric toy utilizing the electric wind for its propulsion was made by E. R. King, an associate of James Wimshurst. This toy, which may be called an "electrical rabbit hunt", is now at the Science Museum in London.

REFERENCES

1. P. Benjamin, *A History of Electricity*, John Wiley and Sons, New York, 1898, pp. 506, 507.
2. J. C. Poggendorff, *Geschichte der Physik*, Johann A. Barth, Leipzig, 1879, p. 846.
3. V. K. Chew, *Physics for Princes*, Her Majesty's Stationery Office, London, 1968, p. 13.
4. B. Wilson, *Philosophical Transactions*, Vol. 51, p. 896 (1760).
5. J. Langenbucher, *Beschreibung einer betriichtlich. verbesserten Elektrisiermaschine*, Mathaus Reigers, Augsburg, 1780, pp. 54-56 and Plate 3.
6. G. Adams, *An Essay on Electricity*, London, 1799, 5th edn., pp. 580-581 and Plate 4.
7. J. Sparks, Ed., *The Works of Benjamin Franklin*, Whittemore, Niles, and Hall, Boston, 1856, Vol. 5, p. 371.
8. M. Guyot, *Nouvelles Recreations Physiques Mathematiques*, Gueffier, Paris, 1786, Vol.1, pp. 249, 250 and Plate 25.
9. H. J. Oosting, *Zeitschrift fur den Physikalischen und Chemischen Unterricht*, Vol. 9, pp. 84-85 (1896).
10. R. Aime, *Annales de Chimie et de Physique*, Ser. 2, Vol. 62, p. 421 (1833).
11. C. Tomlinson, *Philosophical Magazine*, Ser. 4, Vol. 27, p. 202 (1864).
12. M. E. Mascart, *Traite d'Electricite Statique*, G. Masson, Paris, 1876, Vol. 1, pp. 175-179.
13. D. Kampfer, *Annalen der Physik*, Ser. 3,Vo-l 20, pp. 601-614 (1887)
14. E. Bichat, *Annales de Chimie et de Physique*/Vol 12, pp. 64-79 (1887).
15. A. Christenson and S.Moller,*AIIA Journal* Vol. 5, pp.

1768-1733, (1967).

16. L. B. Loeb, *Electrical Coronas,* University California Press, Berkley, 1965, pp. 402-416

17. L. D. Gale, *Elements of Natural Philosophy* Mark H. Newman, New York, 1846, p. 161.

18. A. Neuburger, *Ergotzliches Experimentierbuch,* Ullstein & Co., Berlin, 1920, pp 432.

Chapter 4   FRANKLIN'S SPARK MOTORS AND THEIR DESCENDANTS

If one defines the "electric motor" as a machine capable of converting substantial amounts of electrical energy into mechanical energy, then it was Benjamin Franklin who invented the electric motor, for he was the first person to design and to construct a machine capable of accomplishing such a conversion.

Franklin built two electric motors, which he called "electrical wheels". He described them in a letter to Peter Collinson, Fellow of the Royal Society of London, written in Philadelphia in 1748.[1] His first motor was a big machine, about 40 inches in diameter. The main part of this motor was a wooden disk mounted horizontally on a vertical wooden axle and carrying 30 glass spokes with brass thimbles on their ends (Fig. 20 and Plate 2).The axle turned on a sharp point of iron fixed in its lower end and was kept in the vertical position by a strong wire mounted in its upper end and passing through a small hole in a thin stationary brass plate. Two oppositely charged Leyden jars (bottles) were placed in close proximity to the thimbles on the spokes, so that when the wheel turned, the thimbles barely missed the knobs of the jars. As the thimbles moved past the Leyden jars, a spark jumped between a jar knob and the passing thimble, charging the latter with a charge of the same polarity as that of the knob. Therefore each knob attracted the oncoming thimbles ("opposite charges attract") and repelled the departing thimbles ("like charges repel"), causing the motor to turn. The motor, being perfectly symmetric, could turn in either direction, and usually required a starting push by hand to initiate the charging of the thimbles.

Here is how Franklin himself described the operation of his motor: [1]

"If now the wire of a bottle, electrified in the common way, be brought near the circumference of this wheel, it will attract the nearest thimble, and so put the wheel in motion; that thimble, in passing by, receives a spark, and thereby being electrified, is repelled, and so driven forwards; while a second being attracted, approaches the wire, receives a spark, and is driven after the first, and so on till the wheel has gone once round, when the thimbles before electrified approaching the wire, instead of being attracted as they were at first, are repelled, and the motion presently ceases. But if another bottle, which had been charged through the coating (i.e. charged oppositely to the first, O. J.), be placed near the same wheel, its wire will attract the thimble repelled by the first, and thereby double the force that carries the wheel round; and, not only taking out the fire (electric charge, O. J.) that had been communicated to the thimbles by the first bottle, but even robbing them of their natural quantity, instead of being repelled when they come again towards the first bottle, they are more strongly attracted, so that the wheel mends its pace, till it goes with a great rapidity, twelve or fifteen rounds in a minute, and with such strength, as that the weight of one hundred Spanish dollars, with which we once loaded it, did not seem in the least to retard its motion".

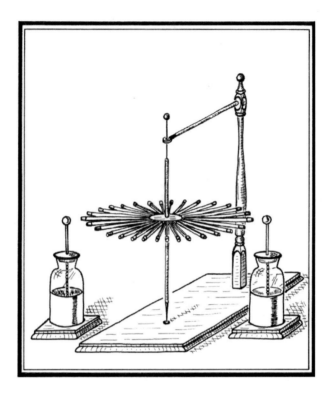

FIGURE 20

Franklin's first "electrical wheel" was the earliest device converting substantial amounts of electrical energy into mechanical energy .

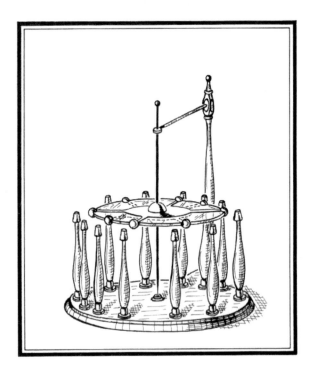

FIGURE 21

Franklin's second "electrical wheel" was more efficient than the first. It was powered by the electric charge stored in its capacitor-rotor.

Franklin was not quite pleased with this motor, however, because it required "a foreign force, to wit, that of the bottles" for its operation. He constructed therefore a second, "self moving", motor, which itself contained the electrical energy to be converted into the mechanical motion.

The second motor was made as follows (Fig. 21 and Plate 3). A disk of window glass, 17 inches in diameter, was gilded on each side, except for narrow areas next to the edge. Several lead spheres (bullets) were fixed to the edge of the disk and were connected in alternation to the two gold layers. The disk was mounted on a vertical axle consisting of two pieces of strong wire, each about 9 inches long; the upper wire being in contact with the top layer of gold, the lower wire being in contact with the bottom layer. The lower wire terminated in a sharp point resting on a piece of brass cemented within a glass salt-cellar. The upper wire passed through a hole in a thin brass plate cemented on a long strong piece of glass. This wire carried a small ball on its upper end for preventing a corona discharge from it. Several glass pillars with thimbles on their tops were positioned in a circle around the disk, so that the spheres on the edge of the disk barely missed the thimbles when the disk was in motion. The motor was powered by electricity stored in the disk itself, which, due to the two layers of gold, constituted a capacitor capable of storing an appreciable quantity of charge (to charge the rotor, the two layers of gold were temporarily connected to an electrostatic friction genera tor).

The motor operated on the same principle as Franklin's

first motor, except that now the thimbles were stationary and received positive or negative charges from the passing spheres, rather than the other way around. As in the first motor, the rotation persisted as long as there was enough charge stored in the capacitor (rotor) to produce sparks between the spheres and the thimbles.

Franklin reported that his second motor (which was more powerful than the first one) could make 50 turns in a minute and could run for up to 30 minutes on a single charging of the rotor.[1] Experiments with replicas of Franklin's motors performed by the author indicate that the original motors developed a power of the order of 0.1 watt,[2,3] which was a very impressive achievement for that very early period in the history of electric science.

Several authors have described simplified versions of Franklin's motors.[4,5] Miniature Franklin-type motors have been constructed and described by A. D.Moore[6] (Fig. 22). One such motor consists of a Plexiglas disk about 4 inches in diameter with small conducting balls embedded in the rim. The disk turns on a horizontal axis supported by a base behind the disk. The motor runs when placed between two conductors connected to an electrostatic generator. To make the motor self-starting and one-way running, the conductors may be provided with short auxiliary rods tangential to the disk; since the rods dispatch sparks predominantly in the direction of their free ends, the disk also turns in this direction. Another little motor of the same type designed by Moore is shown in Fig. 23.

An obvious improvement of Franklin's motors would be to use a cylindrical rotor with electrodes in the shape of long strips. Such electrodes would accept more charge than thimbles or spheres, and the power of the motor would be increased considerably. Motors of this type have indeed been constructed. Here is a description of a "bell jar" motor taken from a book published in 1847 (Fig. 24): "On a pivot, *a,* suspend a bell jar having four pieces of tinfoil pasted on its sides, *b,* c, *d;* connect the jar, by means of the insulated wire, *y,* with the prime conductor (high-voltage terminal of an electrostatic friction generator, O. J.) so that the pieces of tinfoil may receive sparks. On the opposite side arrange a conductor, *x,* in connection with the ground by a chain. On putting the machine into activity, the jar will commence rotating on its pivot."[7]

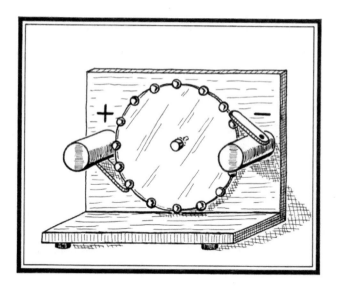

FIGURE 22

Several authors have described simplified versions of Franklin's motors. One such motor consists of a Plexiglas disk about 4 inches in diameter with small conducting balls embedded in the rim. The disk turns on a horizontal axis supported by a base behind the disk.

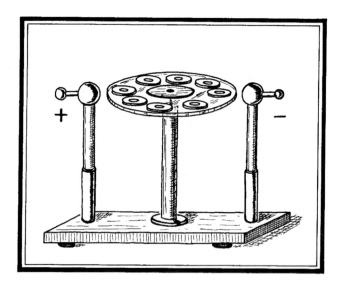

FIGURE 23

This inexpensive miniature Franklin-type motor of recent design can be used for lecture-room demonstrations of electrostatic forces. The rotor disk can be made from cardboard, wood, or plastic. For the rotor electrodes one can use thumbtacks or small aluminum foil disks.

Small motors closely related to both Franklin's first motor and to pendulum motors were used in the rotary-type "perpetuum mobile" (see Chapter 2) operated from a Zamboni pile.[8] The main part of these motors (Fig. 25) was a light insulated arm pivoted on a sharp point and carrying a piece of tinsel on each end. The tinsels could just touch the knobs of the pile when the arm was moving on its pivot. The device functioned in the same manner as Franklin's first motor, the two tinsels corresponding to the thimbles of; the latter.

An analogous design has recently been described a "millifleapower motor" operating from a nuclear battery.[9] In this motor a light aluminum vane with pointed ends (Fig. 26) bent so as to form an inverted V is mounted at its midpoint on the tip of a sharp needle protruding from the positive terminal of the battery. As the vane turns, its ends come close to two spheres connected with the ground through a high resistance and become attracted by them. A discharge from the ends of the vane charges the two spheres, and the spheres then repel the ends of the vane. During the time it takes the vane to complete one half of its revolution, the charges of the spheres leak off to the ground, so that the spheres can again attract the ends of the vane, accept new charges from them, and then again repel them. The motor is expected to run for many years.

An interesting motor derivable from Franklin's first motor and from pendulum motors was suggested for operation from an electrophorus.[10] The main part of this motor (Fig. 27) was a light conducting ring supported in a vertical plane on an insulated needle. In front of the ring there were two insulated spheres, which were so positioned that the ring just missed them as it turned on its needle. The spheres were either charged oppositely by the electrophorus, or only one sphere was charged, in which case the second sphere was grounded. The device operated on the same principle as Franklin's first motor.

Of all the motors discussed above, Franklin's original motors and the bell jar motor were the most powerful ones. One can make such motors even more powerful by increasing the number of moving and stationary electrodes. But this can be done only up to a limit, because if the electrodes are too close to one another, sparks will jump all around from one electrode to the next, thus short-circuiting the motor. The motor will then not work at all, unless the operating voltage is lowered. But by lowering the voltage one also lowers the power, so that the gain obtained by increasing the number of electrodes becomes offset by the decrease in the operating voltage. Franklin type motors have therefore an inherent limitation in their power characteristics, and the fact that they depend for their operation on the presence of many metallic electrodes is one of their disadvantages.

Since in Franklin's motors and in other motors described in this chapter the rotor is charged by means of electric sparks, these motors may be classified as "spark motors". Toward the end of the 19th century a way was found to construct electrostatic motors based on the same mechanism of attraction and repulsion between electric charges as in Franklin's motors, but with rotors (or stators) charged more efficiently than it is possible to do by means of the sparks. These motors are described in the next chapter.

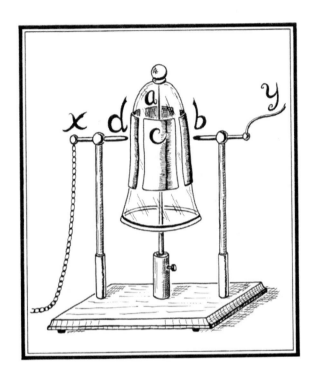

FIGURE 24

This "bell jar" Franklin-type motor had a cylindrical rotor with tin foil electrodes in the shape of long strips.

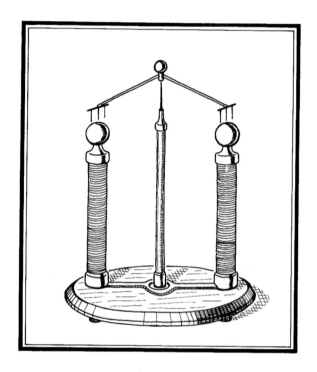

FIGURE 25

This small motor was used as a rotary-type "perpetuum mobile" operating from a Zamboni pile. Such motors continued for years without stopping.

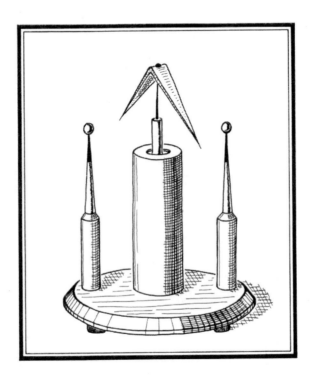

FIGURE 26

An analogous design has recently been described as a
"millifleapower motor" operating from a nuclear battery.[*]

---

[*] See the report on "Nuclear Batteries" published by Integrity Research
Institute for more information on these long-life electron (beta) or
proton (alpha) sources.

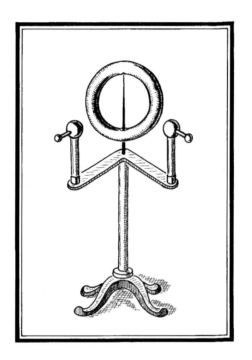

FIGURE 27

This motor derivable from Franklin's first motor and from pendulum motors was suggested for operation from an electrophorus.

REFERENCES

1. J.Sparks, Ed., *The Works of Benjamin Franklin;* Whittemore, Niles, and Hall, Boston, 1856, Vol. 5, pp. 204-207.
2. O. Jefimenko and D. K. Walker, *The Physics Teacher,* Vol. 9, pp. 121-129 (1971).
3. O. Jefimenko, *American Journal of Physics,* Vol. 39, pp. 1139-1140 (1971).
4. M. Guyot, *Nouvelles Recreations Physiques et Mathematiques,* Gueffier, Paris, 1786, Vol. 1, pp. 272-274 and Plate 27.
5. Dayton C. Miller, *Sparks, Lightning, Cosmic Rays,* MacMillan, New York, 1939, pp. 63, 64.
6. A. D. Moore, *Electrostatics,* Doubleday and Company, Inc., New York, 1968, pp. 104-108.
7. J. W. Draper, *Text-Book on Chemistry,* Harper and Brothers, New York, 1847, p. 105.
8. M. J. Jamin, *Cours de Physique,* GauthierVillars, Paris, 1869, 2nd edn., Vol. 3, p. 39.
9. R. H. Dressel, *High School Science Bulletin of the New Mexico State University,* Vol. 6, pp. 3-4 (April 1, 1964)
10. H.Wommelsdorf, *Annalen der Physik,* Ser. 4, Vol. 70, pp. 135-138 (1923).

Chapter 5   CORONA MOTORS AND MOTORS SIMILAR TO THEM

In 1867, W. Holtz, the inventor of the electrostatic "influence" machine (generator) carrying his name, discovered that this machine could function as a motor when powered by another similar machine.[1] In order to study this effect in some detail, the famous German physicist J. C. Poggendorff ordered the construction of a special device, analogous to Holtz's machine, but designed to operate only as a motor and provided with numerous adjustable components so as to operate under a wide range of conditions.[2]

The basic part of this motor was a vertical glass-disk rotor placed between two ebonite crosses carrying metallic sharp-needle "combs" (Fig. 28 and Plate 4). The sharp points of the combs almost touched the surface of the disk, so that the disk could be charged by connected in alternation to an electrostatic generator. Each comb could be oriented so as to make an arbitrary angle with respect to a radial direction. Just like the sparks in Franklin's motors, the corona discharge from a comb deposited on the rotor a charge of the same polarity as that of the comb. Each comb repelled therefore the segment of the rotor carrying charges which it sprayed onto the rotor and attracted the segment carrying charges sprayed onto the rotor by the preceding comb. Because of a continuous discharge between the combs and the rotor, almost the entire surface of the rotor was sprayed with electric charges. The repulsion and attraction between the combs and the rotor, were therefore not only much stronger than in Franklin's motors, (where only the electrodes were charged) but were also much steadier, since the distances between the combs and the charges on the rotor were always the same. As a result, the torque and power obtainable with this motor were far greater than those obtainable with Franklin's motors of similar dimensions.

Poggendorff made a thorough study of his motor, varying all its important parameters (his article comprises 32 pages). He used several rotors of different thickness and surface characteristics, whose weight ranged from 2.5 to 4.5 pounds (all rotors were 15 inches in diameter). He varied the number, the orientation, and the polarity of the co He found that a motor with combs arranged along the radii of the rotor could rotate equally well in either direction but was not self-starting, since such combs sprayed charges onto the rotor in a perfectly symmetric fashion. However, if the combs were slanted relative to the radii, the motor became self-starting and unidirectional, because such combs sprayed charges predominantly in one direction. He also found that the performance of the motor could be improved by placing pieces of glass, cardboard, or metal close to the surface of the rotor (this is the principle of the modern "backing plate" or "lining"; see Chapter 10). When properly adjusted, the motor could run at better than 300 rpm.

Poggendorff had fully appreciated the superiority of his motor in comparison of Franklin's motors, and had stated so at the end of his article. In fact, he had indicated that his motor used from 1200 to 1800 times as much current as Franklin's motors, in which case, assuming that the operating voltage of his motor was the same as that of Franklin's motors (approximately 100 kilovolts), the power of his motor must have been close to 100 watts.

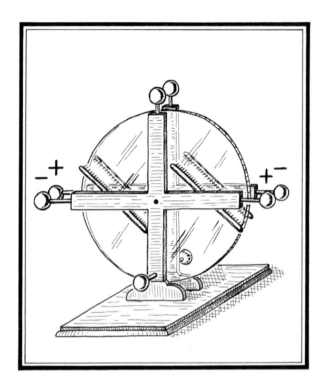

FIGURE 28

Poggendorff's corona motor had a glass-disk rotor placed between two ebonite crosses carrying metallic sharp-needle "combs".

At the time when Poggendorffs article was written, however, it was considered unscientific to expect that electricity *(any* electricity) could ever become a significant source of motive power. This may be the reason why Poggendorff, speaking of the rotation phenomenon that he investigated, declared at the end of his article: " ... it would be a sanguine hope if one wanted to believe that any useful mechanical effect could be achieved with it. That this is not possible, follows already from the consideration of how small is the quantity of electricity that is here put into play in comparison to that developed by a voltaic battery, with which one nevertheless, even with the help of the magnetismus produced by it, has so far achieved nothing substantial ("Erkleckliches")".

The argument was obviously weak, but taking into account Poggendorffs reputation as an eminent scientist, it was probably sufficient to discourage further serious investigations of the corona-induced rotation for many years to come. Since Poggendorff's motor depended on a corona discharge for its operation, the motor may be classified as a "corona motor".

Holtz's rotation phenomenon was also studied by the Danish physicist C. Christiansen (whose interest in the phenomenon had been aroused by a preliminary report of Poggendorffs investigations published in 1867).[3] Christiansen described two motors based on Holtz's discovery. His first motor consisted of a horizontal disk rotor and two stationary corona-producing combs. His second motor was similar to the first except that in it the glass disk was stationary and the combs constituted the rotor. The rotor combs in this second motor were located below the glass disk and were charged by means of two foil strips hanging from them and sliding along two horizontal concentric contact rings mounted on the base of the motor.

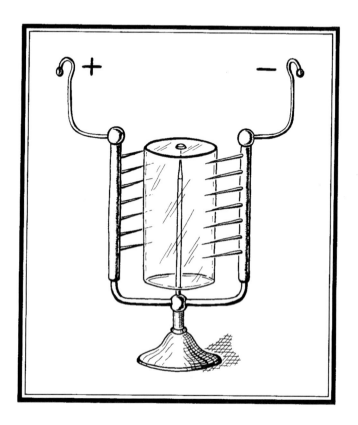

FIGURE 29

This self-starting corona motor with a cylindrical rotor was described in 1871 under the name of " electric tourbillion ".

FIGURE 30

In this hand-held corona motor (attributed to Ruhmkorff) the horizontal wire, by a corona discharge, extracted charges from the power source, and the vertical needle connected to this wire, also by a corona discharge, sprayed these charges onto the rotor.

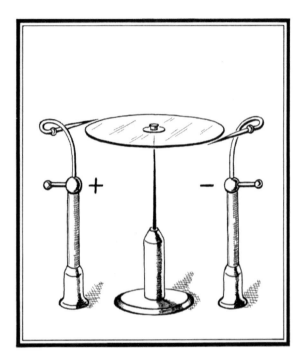

FIGURE 31

This motor had two insulated corona producing points
tangential to the rotor disk and oriented in the same rotational
direction.

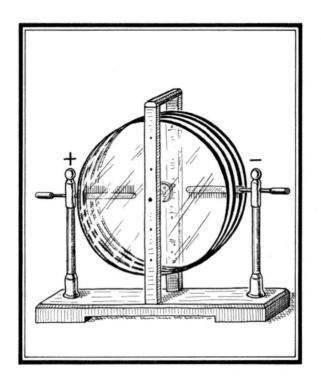

FIGURE 32

This corona motor with a compound glass rotor could run at
about 2000 rpm and had a power of about 90 watts.

Cylindrical and spherical motors operating on the same principle as Poggendorffs motor were described in 1871 by W. Gruel (Fig. 29), who called them the "electric tourbillions".[4] Gruel pointed out that these motors could be made self-starting and unidirectional by inclining the combs in the same rotational direction with respect to the surface of the rotor. He also suggested that by providing the rotors with a series of holes, the motors could be used as sirens. A disk motor not noticeably different from Poggendorffs motor was patented in the U.S.A. in 1891 by J. W. Davis and J. B. Farrington.[5]

An interesting hand-held corona motor (attributed to Ruhmkorff) was described in 1876 by M. E. Mascart.[6] The motor had a horizontal mica disk rotor (Fig. 30) supported on a vertical needle by a jewel bearing, such as are used for supporting compass needles. Below the disk there were two vertical corona-producing needles mounted on a hard rubber base. One of the latter needles was connected to a metal handle; the other was connected to a long, stiff, horizontal wire terminating in a sharp point. To set the motor in motion, the operator held the motor so that the sharp point of the horizontal wire was in the proximity of a charged conductor. By a corona discharge, the horizontal wire then extracted charges from the conductor, and the vertical needle connected to this wire, also by a corona discharge, sprayed these charges onto the rotor. The second vertical needle discharged the rotor and conducted its charges to the ground through the hand and body of the operator.

A number of experiments with Poggendorff type corona motors were reported in 1921 by V. E. Johnson.[7] One of his motors was similar to Ruhmkorff's motor (Fig. 31). This was a horizontal mica disk, about 6 inches in diameter, supported on a vertical needle point. At the edge of the disk there were two insulated corona-producing points tangential to the disk and oriented in the same rotational direction. Another of Johnson's motors was a big machine consisting of two stationary glass disks and a three-piece glass rotor that could rotate on ball bearings between the stationary disks. The rotor was made of two large glass disks separated by a smaller disk so as to have a deep slot along its edge. Two flat sharp-point combs were inserted diametrically opposite to one another into the slot of the rotor (Fig. 32). Johnson estimated that his motor could run at about 2000 rpm and had a power of about 90 watts.

Just as Poggendorffs motor was derived from Holtz's electrostatic machine, a series of electrostatic motors were similarly derived from Wimshurst's electrostatic machine.

In 1891 five such motors were constructed by William McVay of New York City.[8] McVay's first motor (Fig. 33) consisted of two horizontal glass disks, about 12 inches in diameter, one stationary and the other rotating on the vertical axis just above the first. The lower disk had two quadrants of tinfoil, and the upper disk had 16 tinfoil sectors, as shown in the figure. The power (from a Wimshurst machine) was delivered to the motor by means of two insulated arms, each of which terminated in two brushes, one touching continually one of the lower quadrants, the other charging a sector on the upper disk just clear of the edge of the quadrant. Charges of the same polarity were thus deposited on the quadrant and on the sector, causing them to repel each other. An "equalizer" reduced the charge of the sectors before they passed over the further edge of an oppositely charged quadrant, thus reducing the back torque on the rotating disk. An important new feature of this motor was the simultaneous charging of the stationary quadrants and of the moving sectors, which assured a relatively strong starting torque and, together with the neutralizing system, assured a reliable unidirectional operation. McVay also constructed motors of cylindrical geometry, one of which is shown in Fig. 34. In this motor the quadrants were located on the inner cylinder, while the charging and neutralizing brushes were on the neck of the outside cylinder.

McVay's first motor was later modified for charging by combs, rather than by brushes (Fig. 35). The motor then operated essentially as Poggendorffs corona motor, retaining, however, its self-starting and unidirectional qualities.

Instructions for building a Poggendorff motor may be found in the May 1971 issue of *Popular Science*.[9] Instructions for building a simple McVay motor may be found in the January 1914 issue of *Electrical Experimenter*[10] (the author is grateful to Mr. Thorn L. Mayes for this information).

Since a corona discharge in air at atmospheric pressure requires a minimum voltage of about 3000 volts, ordinary corona motors can operate only from sources capable of supplying a voltage of this magnitude. Such voltages are, of course, easily attainable at the present time, and since the corona motors are very simple and efficient devices, they have been further developed and studied in recent years. We shall return to them in the last chapter of this book.

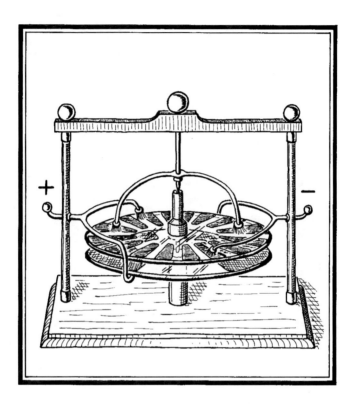

FIGURE 33

McVay's first motor consisted of two horizontal glass disks, about 12 inches in diameter, one stationary and the other rotating on the vertical axis just above the first.

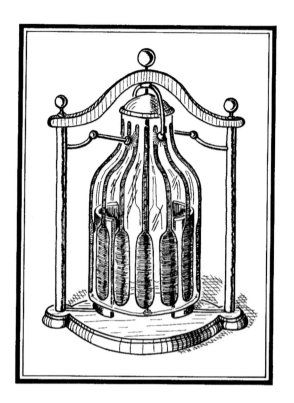

FIGURE 34

In this McVay's motor the quadrants were located on the inner cylinder (shown as two segments), while the charging and neutralizing brushes were on the neck of the outside cylinder.

FIGURE 35

McVay's first motor was later modified for charging by combs, rather than by brushes. The motor then operated essentially as Poggendorff's corona motor, retaining, however, its self-starting and unidirectional qualities.

REFERENCES

1. W. Holtz, *Annalen der Physik,* Ser. 2, Vol. 130, pp. 168-171 (1867).
2. J. C. Poggendorff, *Annalen der Physik,* Ser. 2, Vol. 139, pp. 513-546 (1870).
3. C. Christiansen, *Annalen der Physik,* Ser. 2 Vol. 137, p. 490 (1869).
4. "Elektrischer Tourbillion", *Annalen der Physik,* Ser. 2 Vol. 144, p. 644 (1871).
5. U. S. Patent No. 459678.
6. M.E. Mascart, *Traite d Electricite Statique*, G. Masson, Paris 1876, Vol 1 pp. 179,180.
7. V.E. Johnson, *Modern High Speed Influence Machines*, E and F. N. Spon, London, 1921, pp. 175-205.
8. "A Group of Static Motors" *Electrical World*. Vol. 18 p. 418 (1891)
9. C.P. Gilmore and W.J. Hawkins, *Popular Science Monthly*, Vol. 198 pp. 95-87 and 114. (May 1971).
10. "A Static Electric Motor" *Electrical Experimenter*, January 1914, p. 137.

Chapter 6 CAPACITOR MOTORS

In 1889, Karl Zipernowsky, a Hungarian engineer (co-inventor of practical electrical transformers), constructed a new type of electrostatic motor,[1] which was derived from Thomson's quadrant electrometer.[2] The rotor of this motor (Fig. 36) consisted of two pairs of aluminum sectors insulated from each other and from the rest of the apparatus. The stator consisted of four double (hollow) sectors of brass enclosing the rotor. The rotor was fitted with a commutator in four parts, by means of which the sectors of the rotor were charged oppositely to those sectors of the stator into which they were entering and identically to those sectors of the stator which they were leaving. An interesting property of this motor was that it could operate from high-voltage de as well as from high-voltage ac sources.

Inasmuch as Zipernowsky's motor operated as a result of the electric forces exerted by one charged conducting plate upon a second charged conducting plate (which are the same forces that act upon the two plates of a capacitor) it constituted what is now called an electrostatic "capacitor motor". A simpler version of a capacitor motor was described in 1904 by van Huffel.[3] This motor was based on the so-called Thomson's replenisher.[4] The motor had an essentially cylindrical geometry (Fig. 37) and consisted of a rotor with two insulated bent brass plates mounted on a vertical axle and located between two similar, but slightly larger, plates of the stator. The rotor plates (which were not quite coaxial) were charged by means of two metallic tongues connected to the stator plates; the tongues touched the rotor plates just as the latter began to clear the stator

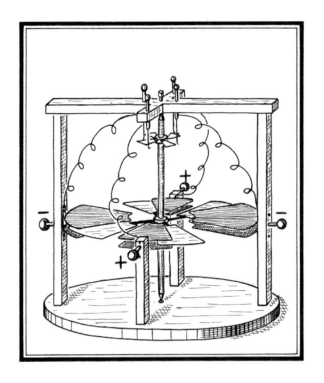

FIGURE 36

This motor was built in 1889 by Karl Zipernowsky, a
Hungarian engineer. It operated from dc as well as from ac
sources.

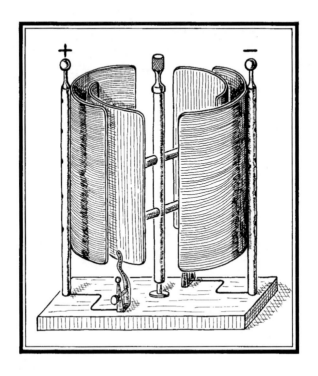

FIGURE 37

This capacitor motor was described in 1904 by van Huffel. Its rotor could be charged by contact or by sparks .

plates. The charging of the rotor plates could occur by a direct contact as well as through a spark, depending on the adjustment of the tongues. Since capacitor motors do not require sparks or a corona discharge for their operation, they can operate, at least in principle, from as Iowa voltage as one desires to use. This is one of their important advantages and is one of the reasons that such motors have been given considerable attention in recent years. Furthermore, as already indicated, capacitor motors can operate not only from de sources, but also from ac sources. Finally, when powered by an ac source, they can operate both as synchronous and asynchronous motors (Zipernowsky's original motor operated from ac as an asynchronous motor). A synchronous capacitor-type electrostatic motor is merely a multi-electrode capacitor motor without a commutator, the proper charging of the rotor being accomplished by continuously supplying an ac voltage of proper frequency between the stator and the rotor (Fig. 38). It is easy to see that if the rotor moves by one electrode in one period of the supply voltage, then the ac voltage accomplishes the same effect as that accomplished by a de voltage with a commutator. The synchronous velocity is therefore $2\pi f/N$, where f is the frequency of the supply voltage and N is the number of the electrodes.

Several precision-made synchronous motors were described in 1969 by B. Bollee.[5] One of these motors ran on sapphire bearings and had a cylindrical aluminum rotor 1 centimeter long and 0.45 centimeters in diameter; the rotor and the stator had 60 electrodes each, with a 0.001 centimeter gap between stator and rotor electrodes. The maximum power of this motor was about 100 microwatts at 220 volts and 50 hertz. Another motor (for an electric clock) had a dielectric disk rotor, with four rows of 100

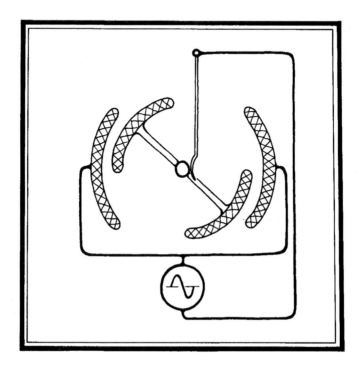

FIGURE 38

In a synchronous capacitor-type electrostatic motor the proper charging of the rotor is accomplished by continuously supplying an ac voltage of proper frequency between the stator and the rotor.

FIGURE 39

This synchronous electrostatic motor is essentially a variable capacitor with a rotatable shaft. The design of this motor is similar to the design of an electrostatic variable-capacitance generator.

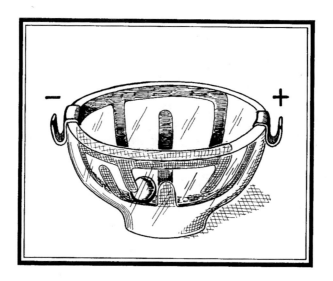

FIGURE 40

This interesting motor has been described by Moore, who calls it the "Interdigital Motor". The stator consists of a glass bowl with strips of aluminum foil glued to it. The rotor is a single conducting ball inside the bowl.

electrodes on each side, located between two bearing covers, each 'with five rows of 100 electrodes; the gap width in the axial direction was 0.01 centimeter.

At 200 volts this motor had a maximum output of 600 microwatts. An interesting feature of this motor was that it had no slip ring on the rotor shaft, and that the rotor was therefore not connected to the power source. Instead, the stator was divided into two mutually insulated halves. This arrangement reduced the friction of the rotor and improved the performance of the motor. Still another motor was essentially a variable capacitor with a rotatable shaft. It had 15 plates in the stator and 14 in the rotor, each 0.03 centimeters thick; the gaps between stator and rotor plates were 0.015 centimeters (Fig. 39). The design of this motor is similar to the design of the electrostatic variable-capacitance generator described by N. J. Felici.[6]

According to Bollee, the maximum average torque on the rotor in a capacitor-type electrostatic motor is $T_{max} = kNV^2$, where k is a geometrical constant, and V is the peak voltage applied. A motor with many electrodes is therefore slow but produces greater torque. The power of the motor is proportional to the square of the applied voltage and to the frequency but does not depend on the number of electrodes.

An important parameter in capacitor-type electrostatic motors is the capacitance difference $C_{max} - C_{min}$, where C_{max} is the greatest capacitance between the rotor and the stator and C_{min} is the smallest capacitance as they occur when the rotor turns. The larger this parameter is, the better are both the torque and the power. The main objective in the design of such motors is therefore to obtain the greatest possible variation of the capacitance.

An interesting motor which can be classified either as a modified Franklin's second motor or as a modified capacitor-type motor has been described by Moore[7] who calls it the Interdigital Motor. The stator consists of a glass bowl with strips of aluminum foil glued to it (Fig. 40). The rotor is a single conducting ball inside the bowl; the ball runs along the sloping side when the strips are connected to an electrostatic generator (positive and negative strips are connected in alternation). Several balls can be placed into the bowl at the same time, and all of them will then run.

REFERENCES

1. "Zipernowsky Electrostatic Motor", *Electrical World,* Vol. 14, p. 260 (1889).

2. W. Thomson, *British Association Report, 1855* (2), p. 22.
3. W. Thomson, *British Association Report, 1855* (2), p. 22.
4. N. G. van Huffel, *Zeitschrift fur den Physikalischen und Chemischen Unterriclit,* Vol. 17, pp. 316-317 (1904).

5. B. Bollee, *Philips Technical Review,* Vol. 30, pp. 178-194 (1969).
6. N. J. Felici, *Electronics and Power,* Vol. 11, pp. 169-171 (1965).
7. A. D. Moore, *Electrostatics,* Doubleday and Company, Inc., New York, 1968, p. 109.

Chapter 7   INDUCTION MOTORS

In 1892-1893, electrostatic motors of a fundamentally new kind were described by Riccardo Arno[1,2] and by W. Weiler.[3] Their motors operated on the principle that the polarization of a dielectric in a variable electric field lags behind the field inducing the polarization. Therefore if a dielectric body is placed into a rotating electric field, the polarization charges* induced on the body will experience a force causing the body to follow the rotation of the field.

Arno's motor (Fig. 41) had a cylindrical stator formed by four insulated copper segments enclosing the space in which the rotating field was to be produced. The rotor was a hollow closed ebonite cylinder supported on two steel points turning in holes in glass; the cylinder weighed 40.33 grams, was 18 centimeters long and 8 centimeters in diameter. The rotating field was produced by means of a high-voltage transformer (3800 volts output), an RC-circuit, and a mercury commutator. The rotor attained a speed of about 250 rpm and developed a torque of 176 centimeter$^2 \times$gram$\times$second^{-2} (or 17.6 μN-m, using the more common units of N-m for torque, where a Newton of force equals kg$\times$m/s^2 – Ed. Note)

Weiler used a hand-operated double commutator for his motors. The commutator delivered high voltage from an electrostatic generator in sequence to the four segments of a stator, thus producing the needed rotating electric field.

*See, for example, O. Jefimenko "Electricity and Magnetism", Appleton-Century-Crofts, Inc. (1966), pp. 245-249

Weiler described four different motors utilizing rotating fields. One of his motors was similar to Arno's motor. The operation of this motor (and that of Arno's motor) can be explained with the aid of Fig. 42, representing the top view of the motor. When segment A of the stator is positive, and segment B is negative, the electric field of the stator induces in the dielectric rotor (assumed to be at rest) polarization charges as shown in the figure. After the commutator has completed 1/4 revolution, segment C is positive and segment D is negative. Thus the field has rotated by 90^0, and now it polarizes the rotor in a new direction (at 90^0 with respect to the first). However, since it takes a certain time for the polarization charges to relax to zero, some of the initial polarization charges are still on the rotor, so that the distribution of the polarization charges on the rotor is not symmetrical relative to the charges on the stator. The rotor experiences therefore a torque due to attraction and repulsion between the rotor charges and stator charges, and the rotor turns.

Weiler also experimented with motors having noncylindrical rotors. One such motor is shown in Fig. 43. Rotating field electrostatic motors with disk-shaped rotors were built and studied between 1894 and 1901 in Japan by Hiderato Ho.[4] Since Arno's and Weilers motors depend for their operation on induced polarization charges, they may be called "induction motors".

Induction motors, too, have a number of appealing features which attracted considerable interest to such motors in recent years: the motors can operate from both dc and ac; the motors can operate from low-voltage sources; since the motors require no brushes or slip rings, friction losses in these motors are very small.

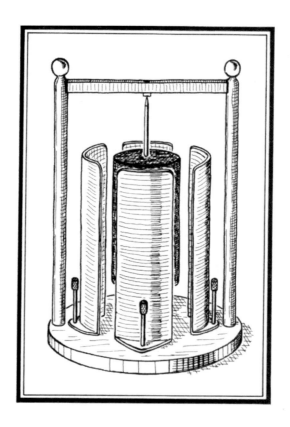

FIGURE 41

Arno's induction motor operated on the principle that the
polarization of a dielectric in a variable electric field lags
behind the field.

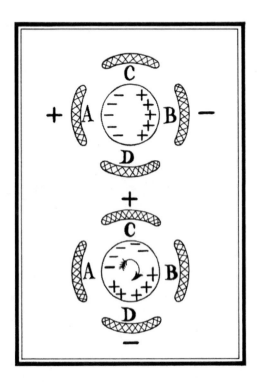

FIGURE 42

The operation of Arno's and Weiler's induction motors
can be explained with the aid of this diagram.

FIGURE 43

In 1892-1893, Weiler also experimented with induction
motors having noncylindrical rotor, such as the motor
shown in this drawing. Induction motors have a number
of appealing features which attracted considerable interest
to such motors in recent years.

Several carefully designed induction motors (both cylindrical and flat) were described in 1969 by Bollee.[5] One such motor of cylindrical geometry operated from a three-phase power supply at 220 volts and 50 hertz. The stator had 12 electrodes, which surrounded a rotor 15 centimeters in diameter. A disk-type induction motor operating from a three-phase power supply had a rotor consisting of 10 glass disks, each 6 centimeters in diameter, coated with a thin layer of slightly conductive material and mounted on a common axle. The rotor turned inside a ring formed by 60 comb-shaped stator electrodes. The maximum torque was 2000 centimeter^2 × gram × second^{-2} at 220 volts and 50 hertz[*]. Another interesting motor described by Bollee was a linear induction motor, which "may be regarded as a segment of rotating-field motor bent straight".[5] An extensive mathematical analysis of the induction motors was published in 1970 by Soon Dal Choi and D. A. Dunn.[6] They tested their theoretical results on a cylindrical motor with 72 electrodes. The motor was 14 inches wide, 14 inches high, and 19¼ inches long. It had a Plexiglas rotor that turned at a maximum rate of about 1000 rpm when powered by a 10-kilovolt source.

---

[*] Ed. Note: this is equal to 200 microN-m.

REFERENCES

1. R. Arno, *Rediconti della AttiReale Accademia dei Lincei,* Vol. 1 (2), p. 284 (1892).
2. R. Arno, *The Electrician,* Vol. 29, pp. 516-518 (1892).
3. W. Weiler, *Zeitschrift fur den Physikalischen und Chemischen Unterricht,* Vol. 7, pp. 1-4 (1893).
4. "A Rotary Field Electrostatic Induction Motor", *Electrical World,* Vol. 37, pp. 1012-1014 (1901).
5. B. Bollee, *Philips Technical Review,* Vol. 30, pp. 178-194 (1969).
6. S. D. Choi and D. A. Dunn, *Proceedings of the IDEE,* Vol. 59, pp. 737-738 (1971).

Chapter 8 LIQUID-IMMERSED MOTORS

In 1893, W. Weiler discovered that a glass cylinder placed in a poorly conducting liquid between two spherical electrodes began to rotate when the electrodes were connected to an electrostatic generator. He then constructed a small motor based on this discovery (Fig. 44). The principle of the operation of this motor was essentially the same as that of a cylindrical corona motor, except that the charges were now deposited on the rotor not by a corona discharge, but by the conduction current in the liquid.

In 1896, G. Quincke reported the same phenomenon and published a very comprehensive experimental study of it.[2] His device is shown in a simplified form in Fig. 45. It is interesting to note that Quincke, rather than Weiler, has been credited by subsequent investigators with the discovery of the rotation of dielectric bodies in poorly conducting liquids. Weiler-type liquid-immersed dielectric motors were recently studied in considerable detail by P. E. Seeker and his co-workers.[3,4] Their motors operated in various semi-insulating liquids such as hexane, hexane doped with amyl alcohol or ethyl alcohol, and isoamyl alcohol. In one of their motors the electrodes were stainless steel squares 1.8 centimeters on a side. Their separation was varied from 1 to 2.5 centimeters. The rotor, of ebonite or Perspex, was 0.95 centimeters in diameter and 2.2 centimeters long. The operating voltage was from 3 to 30 kilovolts. The speed of the motor was found to be a linear function of the applied voltage, with the maximum recorded speed of about 2500 rpm.

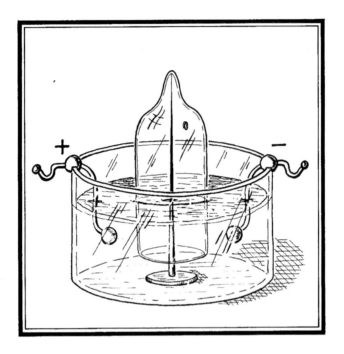

FIGURE 44

In 1893, W. Weiler discovered that a glass cylinder placed in poorly conducting liquid between two spherical electrodes began to rotate when the electrodes were connected to an electrostatic generator.

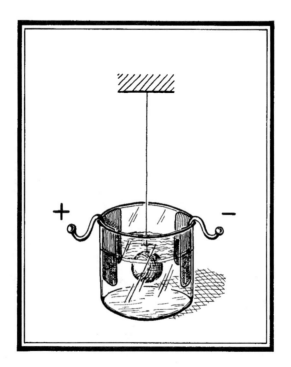

FIGURE 45

In 1896, G. Quincke reported the same phenomenon of rotation and published a very comprehensive experimental study of it. His liquid immersed motor is shown in a simplified form in the above drawing.

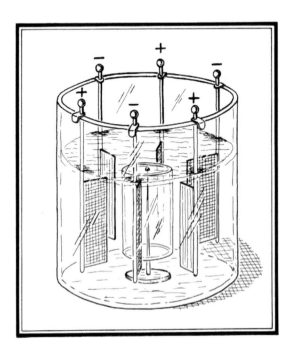

FIGURE 46

This liquid-immersed dielectric motor was recently studied in considerable detail by P.E. Secker and his co-workers.

In another motor, a stator with six electrodes was used (Fig. 46). The rotor was made of Perspex and was 7/8 inches in diameter and 2 inches long; it had a layer of high-permittivity material on its surface (titanium ceramic in polystyrene). Powered by a 30-kilovolt source, the motor turned at 1700 rpm, and the total power input amounted to 5.4 watts, of which 2.7 watts appeared at the rotor shaft.

A discussion of electrohydrodynamic effects that may take place during an operation of liquid-immersed motors has been presented by J. R. Melcher and G. I. Taylor.[5]

Because of considerable hydrodynamic losses, the motors of this type will apparently always have a relatively low output torque.

REFERENCES

1. W. Weiler, *Zeitschrift fur den Physikalischen und Chemischen Unterricht,* Vol. 6, pp. 194- 195 (1893).
2. G. Quineke, *Annalen der Physik,* Ser. 3, Vol. 59, pp. 417-486 (1896).
3. P. E. Seeker and 1. N. Scialom, *Journal of Applied Physics,* Vol. 39, pp. 2957-2961 (1968).
4. P. E. Seeker and M. R. Belmont, *Journal of Physics D: Applied Physics,* Vol. 3, pp. 216- 220 (1970).
5. J. R. Melcher and G. 1. Taylor, *Annual Review of Fluid Mechanics,* Vol. 1, pp. 111-146 (1969)

Chapter 9   ELECTRET MOTORS

In general, an electret is a *permanently charged dielectric body*. In a more restricted sense of the word, an electret is a permanently polarized dielectric body and may be considered to constitute the electrical counterpart of a permanent magnet. It is this latter type of electret that has been used for constructing electrostatic motors.[*]

In 1961, the Russian physicist A. N. Gubkin described an electret motor[1] shown schematically in Fig. 47. The motor consisted of a stator formed by two horizontal, axially symmetric, parallel-plate capacitors and a rotor formed by two flat, axially symmetric, oppositely polarized electrets mounted on a vertical axle and capable of passing between the plates of the capacitors. The motor operated as follows. When a voltage was applied to the two capacitors, so that plates A and D were positive and plates B and C were negative, the capacitors attracted the electrets as soon as the latter came close to the plates, and the electrets were pulled into the capacitors. A commutator changed the polarity of the plates just as the electrets were coming out from the capacitors, and the electrets were then repelled from them, and so on. Thus the rotor was set in a continuous rotation.

A well-known property of electrets is that they lose their polarization in the absence of adequate shielding. Electret motors with almost perfect shielding were

----

[*] Paraffin is one example of an electret which Dr. Jefimenko used in his research.   – Ed. Note

described by this author and by D. K. Walker in 1970.[2] These motors were based on the so-called "electret slot effect".[3] The slot effect works as follows (Fig. 48). An electret is placed between two pairs of electrodes, each pair forming a slot. If a voltage is applied to one or both electrode pairs, the electret (or the electrodes) experiences a force in a direction perpendicular to the slot and parallel to the plates. This arrangement insures both a nearly perfect shielding and a relatively large force.

A simple electret motor utilizing the slot effect is shown in Fig. 49 and Plate 5.[*] It uses a disk-shaped carnauba wax electret rotor consisting of two oppositely polarized half-disks. The stator has two pairs of electrodes connected to a cylindrical commutator. The thickness of the rotor is 1/2 inch, the diameter is 5 inches. The motor operates from an 8-kilovolt power supply and rotates at 1500 rpm. Similar motors with stationary electrets and rotating electrodes are shown in Plates 6 and 7.

A more sophisticated slot-effect motor[2] uses a cylindrical electret (Fig. 50 and Plate 8). The electret is stationary; it is shaped as a hollow cylinder and has four sections of opposite radial polarization. The rotor is made of four internal and four external aluminum electrodes forming two cylinders with four slots in each. The inner electrodes are cross-connected with the outer ones, and all electrodes

---

[*]The motor was designed by the author and built by one of his students, Charles Lynn Walls, in 1966.

are supported by a Plexiglas disk mounted on a steel axle. This motor uses no commutator. The power is delivered to two adjacent external electrodes by means of two sharp points which charge the rotor through a corona discharge. The overall diameter of this motor is 3 inches, the operating voltage is 6 kilovolts, the speed is up to 5000 rpm, the power is about <u>20 milliwatts</u>.

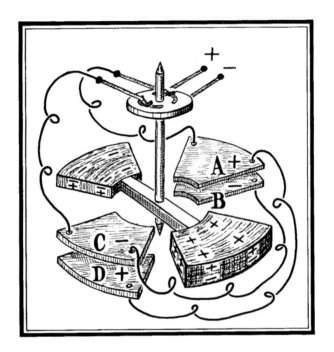

FIGURE 47

In 1961, the Russian physicist A. N. Gubkin described this motor with two electrets in the rotor and two parallel-plate capacitors in the stator. A commutator was used to change the polarity of the capacitors.

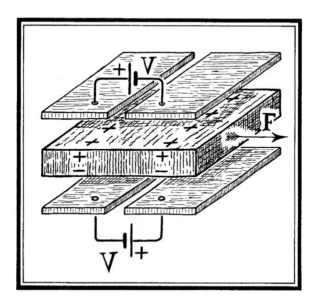

FIGURE 48

The slot effect works as follows. An electret is placed between two pairs of electrodes, each pair forming a slot. If a voltage is applied to one or both electrode pairs, the electret experiences a force in a direction perpendicular to the slot and parallel to the plates.

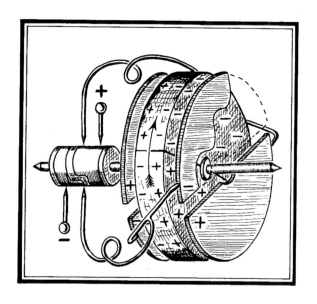

FIGURE 49

This simple electret motor utilizes the slot effect. The rotor is
made of a disk-shaped electret consisting of two oppositely
polarized half-disks. The stator has two pairs of slotted
electrodes connected to a cylindrical commutator, which is
charged by contact or by sparks.

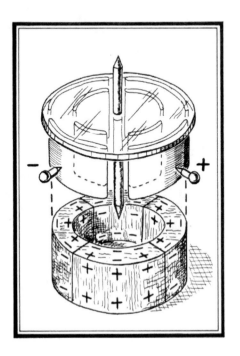

FIGURE 50

This more advanced slot-effect motor uses a stationary cylindrical electret and works without a commutator. The rotor has 8 slots.

FIGURE 51

In this simplified version of a synchronous electret motor
for electric clocks, a thin plastic electret disk with several
active sectors and several cut-outs is used as the rotor.

Synchronous electret motors for electric clocks have been recently announced by the General Time Corporation. The motors are about 1¼ inches in diameter and ¼ inch thick. In these motors (Fig. 51) a thin plastic electret disk with 15 active sectors and 15 equally large cut-outs is the rotor. The rotor is placed between two stator plates fabricated as printed circuit boards. Each stator plate has 30 electrodes connected in alternation to the two input terminals. The operation of this motor is similar to that of the first slot-effect motor described above (Fig. 49) except that the reversal of polarity of the electrodes is accomplished directly by the applied ac voltage rather than by a commutator.

Of all presently known types of electrostatic motors, electret motors are the newest and (together with corona motors) the most highly promising ones. We shall return to them once again in the next chapter.

REFERENCES

1. A. N. Gubkin, *Electrets,* Academy of Sciences, Moscow, 1961, pp. 130-133 (in Russian).
2. O. Jefimenko and D. K. Walker, *Conference on Dielectric Materials, Measurements and Applications,* The Institution of Electrical Engineers, London, 1970, pp. 146-149.
3. O. Jefimenko, *Proceedings of the West Virginia Academy of Sciences,* Vol. 40, pp. 345-348 (1968).

Chapter 10   WHAT TO EXPECT FROM ELECTROSTATIC MOTORS

Having described the various types of electrostatic motors we shall now present a brief discussion of the current aims in the electrostatic motor research and a brief discussion of the most probable future uses and applications of these motors.

It has been pointed out by Bollee[1] that electromagnetic motors rapidly lose their efficiency in scaled-down versions (which is due to the relative increase in energy dissipation in the magnet coils) and that very small capacitor-type and induction-type electrostatic motors may be a better choice for miniaturized systems. Therefore one may expect that miniature electrostatic motors of these types will find applications in various sensor and control devices where only very small torques and power are needed.

Experiments with electret motors conducted in the author's laboratory[2] indicate that these motors may be very useful in systems where powers of up to 1 watt are needed. The most promising electrostatic motors appear to be, however, the corona motors. These motors possess a number of highly desirable features. Here are some of them: the motors are extremely simple in design; they require no expensive materials; their maintenance is very simple; having only few metal parts they possess a very good power-to-weight ratio; they are fully capable of developing appreciable amounts of power; and they can attain very high speeds.

Our present-day awareness of the many attractive properties of corona motors is to a great extent due to the work of the Russian engineers Yu Karpov, V. Krasnoperov, and Yu. Okunev published in 1958 and 1960.[3,4] They described a 6-watt cylindrical corona motor of improved design (Fig. 52) operating from a 7-kilovolt power supply and turning at a rate of 6000 rpm. This motor had a hollow Plexiglas rotor 10.5 centimeters in diameter and 17 centimeters long with a conducting lining on its inner surface. The stator supported 16 knife-like electrodes inclined relative to the surface of the rotor in the direction of the desired rotation. The lining of the rotor served to increase the electric field in the gap between the electrodes and the surface of the rotor and thus to enhance the corona discharge from the electrodes.

A high-speed corona motor with a disk rotor and circumferential electrodes was described by J. D. N. Van Wyck and G. J. Kuhn of South Africa in 1961.[5] The motor (Fig. 53) had a rotor 1.5 inches in diameter turning in jewel bearings. The stator supported 6 sharp-point electrodes. Operating from 8-13 kilovolts, the motor developed speeds of up to 12000 rpm. A similar motor was studied in Poland by B. Sujak and W. Heffner in 1963.[6]

A number of advanced corona motors were studied in the author's laboratory;[7] an example of these motors is given in Fig. 54 and Plate 9. A diagram of a linear corona motor designed by the author is shown in Fig. 55. Instructions for building the corona motors of the author's design may be found in the May 1971 issue of *Popular Science*.[8]

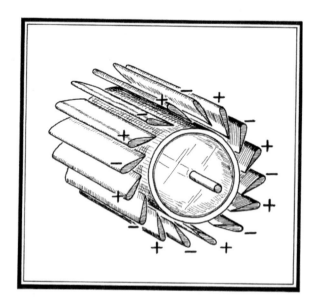

FIGURE 52

In 1958, the Russian engineers Yu. Karpov, V. Krasnoperov, and Yu. Okunev described a 6-watt cylindrical corona motor of an improved design operating from a 7-kilovolt power supply and turning at a rate of 6000 rpm. This motor had a Plexiglas rotor.

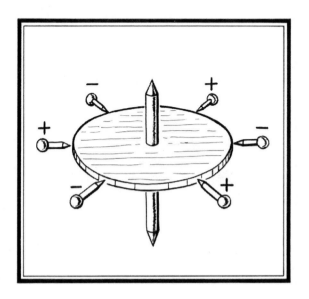

FIGURE 53

This corona motor with a disk rotor and circumferential electrodes was described by J.D.N. Van Wyck and G.J. Kuhn of South Africa in 1961. It had a rotor 1.5 inches in diameter turning in jewel bearings. Operating from 13 kilovolts, the motor ran at 12,000 rpm.

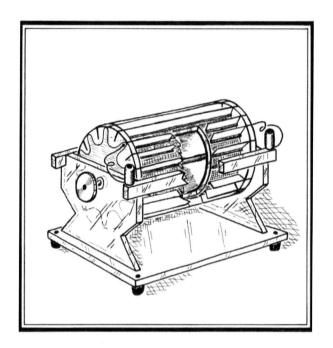

FIGURE 54

The performance of a corona motor depends on the shape and arrangement of electrodes and the structure of the rotor. The curved electrodes of this motor produce an especially large torque. The lining of the rotor increases the power.

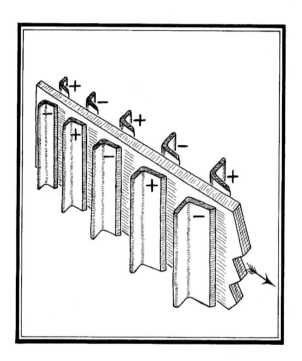

FIGURE 55

The mechanism of electric interaction producing rotational motion in corona motors can be used to achieve a translational motion as well. This drawing shows the principle of a linear corona motor with multiple electrodes.

It appears that corona motors with input power of 100 to 1000 watts and efficiency of at least 60% can be constructed without any difficulty. There seems to be no reason why even more powerful corona motors could not be built. It is likely that the motors can be further improved by using rotors immersed in a gas other than the air at atmospheric pressure.

Performance characteristics of corona motors strongly depend on the design and geometrical configuration of the electrodes spraying charges onto the rotor. Several typical electrode types and electrode configurations for corona motors are shown in Fig. 56. Especially interesting is the electrode arrangement shown in Fig. 56c.

This arrangement is used in conjunction with thin disk-shaped rotors "sandwiched" between two insulating stator plates. An even number of windows is cut in each stator plate, and metal foil electrodes are glued to the walls of the holes, as shown by heavy lines in Fig. 56c. In this arrangement there is a dielectric medium on one side of each electrode, and there is air on the other side. Therefore the electrodes spray charges predominantly in the direction of the side facing the air. Thus a motor with electrodes of this type is unidirectional and self-starting. Furthermore, the entire "sandwich" comprising the rotor and the two stator plates may be very thin. Therefore many such "sandwiches" can be placed on a single axle thus forming a compound motor in which good use is made of the entire volume occupied by the motor. There are indications that compound motors of this type can develop *up to 1000 horsepower for each cubic meter of their volume.*

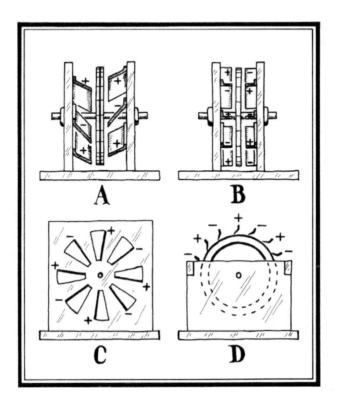

FIGURE 56

(a) Slanted electrodes and disk rotor with a conducting lining in the middle; (b) Straight electrodes; (c) Foil electrodes shielded on one side; (d) Curved electrodes and cylindrical rotor with a conducting lining.

FIGURE 57

Small electrostatic motors can be powered from atmospheric electricity by means of simple earth-field antennas. Whether or not it will be possible to operate large motors in this matter will depend on how successful we are in designing antennas capable of extracting appreciable power from the earth's electric field.[*]

---

[*] Dr. Jefimenko contributed a paper to the 1999 First International Conference on Future Energy in which he stated the potential energy available from the earth's atmospheric electric field was in the hundreds of gigawatts (see Appendix). – Ed. note

An important property of electrostatic motors is that they can operate from a much greater variety of sources than the electromagnetic motors. It is, of course, obvious that any sources used for operating conventional electromagnetic motors can be used to operate the electrostatic motors. However, the electrostatic motors can operate also from sources from which no other motors can operate. The reason for this is that the electrostatic motors are extra-high impedance devices and thus require extremely small currents for their operation.

One very interesting source of electricity for electrostatic motors is the ordinary capacitor. It is true that capacitors, as we know them now, do not store appreciable amounts of electric energy. However, if high-permittivity low-loss dielectric materials were developed, then the capacitor would become a very useful device for storage of electric energy, and possibly could be used in place of the chemical batteries for operating electrostatic motors. Another possible source of power for electrostatic motors are high-impedance high-voltage batteries of the type of Zamboni pile.

A potentially very important source of electricity for powering electrostatic motors are electrostatic generators. Considerable advances in the development of such generators have been made in recent years[9],[10] and it is conceivable that electrostatic motor-generators will be used to convert the high-voltage de produced by such generators into the conventional low-voltage dc or ac.

Finally, a very interesting source for powering electrostatic motors is the atmospheric electric field. In fact, it appears possible to extract the energy contained in this field by means of electrostatic motors. Experiments on such an energy extraction have been conducted by the author.[11,12] In these experiments an electret motor and a corona motor were powered by *simple earth-field antennas* (Fig. 57; Plates 10 to 12). The corona motor was the one shown in Plate 9. The electret motor was similar to that shown in Fig. 49, but with the electret stationary and the electrodes rotating (Plate 6). These experiments indicate that it is entirely possible to operate small electrostatic motors from atmospheric electricity. Whether or not it will be possible to operate large motors in this manner will depend on how successful we will be in designing and building earth-field antennas capable of extracting appreciable power from the earth electric field.

In conclusion it may be useful to mention that a quantitative electrostatic motor research is now only in its very rudimentary stage. Almost all papers on electrostatic motors published thus far deal with the qualitative aspects of the performance of the various types of motors. Only very few papers deal with the optimization of design and with the quantitative aspects of the operation of the motors, likewise only very few papers present a theoretical analysis of the electrostatic motors. It is clear therefore that the electrostatic motors still constitute an essentially unexplored area of physics and engineering, and that the electrostatic motor research is presently one of the potentially most rewarding research fields in modern electrostatics.[*]

---

[*] Electret motors with atmospheric antennas are an untapped and underutilized source of free electrical energy that work very well in dry climates. They should be a part of every renewable energy portfolio in the appropriate environments where they work the best.   – Ed. note

REFERENCES

1. B. Bollee, *Philips Technical Review*, Vol. 30, pp. 178-194 (1969)
2. O. Jefimenko and D. K. Walker, Conference on Dielectric Materials, Measurements and Applications, the Institution of Electrical Engineers, London, 1970, pp. 146-149.
3. Yu. Karpov, V. Krasnoperov, and Yu. Okunev, *Tekhnika Molodezhi,* Vol. 26, pp. 36-37 (Sept. 1958) (in Russian).
4. Yu. Karpov, V. Krasnoperov, Yu. T. Okunev, and V. V. Pasynkov, "On the Motion of Dielectrics in an Electric Field", in *Dielectric Physics,* Academy of Sciences, Moscow, 1960, pp. 124-131 (in Russian).
5. J. D. N. Van Wyck and G. J. Kuhn, *Nature,* Vol. 192, pp. 640-650 (1961).
6. B. Sujak and W. Heffner, *Acta Physica Polonica,* Vol. 23, pp. 715-726 (1963).
7. O. Jefimenko and H. Fischbach-Nazario, *Proceedings of the West Virginia Academy of Sciences,* Vol. 42, pp. 216-221 (1971).
8. C. P. Gilmore and W. J. Hawkins, *Popular Science Monthly,* Vol. 198, pp. 95-97, 114 (May 1971).
9. N. J. Felici, *Elektrostatische Hochspannungs Generatoren,* G. Braun, Karlsruhe, 1957.
10. J. Hughes and P. Seeker, *New Scientist and Science Journal,* Vol. 49, pp. 468-470 (1971).
11. O. Jefimenko, *American Journal of Physics,* Vol. 39, pp. 776-778 (1971).
12. W. Aston, *West Virginia University Magazine,* Vol. 3, Number 4, Spring 1971, pp. 6-11.

APPENDIX

Reprint from *Popular Science* April 1971

The Amazing Motor That Draws Power from the Air

By C.P. Gilmore & William J. Hawkins

Would you believe an electric motor made almost entirely of plastic? That can run on power transmitted through open air? And sneak free electricity right out of the earth's electrical field?

At the University of West Virgina we saw a laboratory full of such exotic devices spinning, humming, and buzzing away like a swarm of bees. They are electrostatic motors, run by charges similar to those that make your hair stand on end when you comb it on a cold winter's day.

Today, we use electromagnetic motors almost exclusively. but electrostatics have a lot of overlooked advantages. They're far lighter per horsepower than electromagnetics, can run at extremely high speeds, and are incredibly simple and foolproof in construction.

"And, in principle," maintains Dr Oleg Jefimenko, "they can do anything electromagnetic motors can do, and some things they can do better."

Jewel-Like Plastic Motors

Jefimenko puts on an impressive demonstration. He showed us motors that run on the voltage developed when you hold them in your hands and scuff across a carpet, and other heavier, more powerful ones that could do real work. Up on the roof of the University's physics building in a blowing snowstorm, he connected an electrostatic motor to a specially designed earth-field antenna. It twirled merrily from electric power drawn out of thin air.

These remarkable machines are almost unknown today. Yet the world's electric motor was an electrostatic. It was invented in 1748 by Benjamin Franklin.

Franklin's motor took advantage of the fact that like charges repel, unlike ones attract. He rigged a wagon-wheel-sized, horizontally mounted device with 30 glass spokes. On the end of each spike was a brass thimble. Two oppositely charged Leyden jars -- high voltage capacitors -- were so placed that the thimbles on the rotating spokes barely missed the knobs on the jars (see photo).

As a thimble passed close to a jar, a spark leaped from knob to thimble. That deposited a like charge on the thimble, so they repelled each other. Then, as the thimble approached the oppositely charged jar, it was attracted. As it passed this second jar, a spark jumped again, depositing a new charge, and the whole repulsion-attraction cycle

132

began again.

In 1870, the German physicist J.C. Poggendorff built a motor so simple it's hard to see what makes it work. The entire motor, as pictured here, is a plastic disk (Poggendorff used glass) and two electrodes. The electrodes set up what physicists call a corona discharge; their sharp edges ionize air molecules that come in contact with them. These charged particles floating through the air charge the surface of the plastic disk nearby. Then the attraction-repulsion routine that Franklin used takes place.

A few papers on electrostatic motors have trickled out of the laboratories in recent years. But nobody really showed much interest until Dr Jefimenko came on the scene.

The Russian-born physicist was attending a class at the University of Gottingen one day shortly after World War II when the lecturer, a Prof. R.W. Pohl, displayed two yard-square metal plates mounted on the end of a pole. He stuck the device outside and flipped it 180 degrees. A galvanometer hooked to the plates jumped sharply.

"I could never forget that demonstration," said Jefimenko. "And I wondered why, if there is electricity in the air, you couldn't use it light a bulb or something."

Electricity Everywhere

The earth's electrical field has been known for centuries. Lightning and St Elmo's fire are the most dramatic manifestations of atmospheric electricity. But the field doesn't exist just in the vicinity of these events; it's everywhere.

The earth is an electrical conductor. So is the ionosphere, the layer of ionized gas about 70 kilometers over our heads. The air between is a rather poor insulator. Some mechanisms not yet explained constantly pumps large quantitites of charged particles into the air. The charged particles cause the electrical field that Jefimenko saw demonstrated. Although it varies widely, strength of the field averages 120 volts per meter.

You can measure this voltage with an earth-field antenna -- a wire with a sharp point at the top to start a corona, or with a bit of radioactive materials that ionizes the air in its immediate vicinity near the earth, voltage is proportional to altitude; on an average day you might measure 1200 volts with a 10-meter antennas.

Over that past few years, aided by graduate-student Henry Fischbach-Nazario, Jefimenko designed advanced corona motors. With David K. Walker, he experimented with electret motors. An electret is an insulator with a permanent electrostatic charge. It produces a permanent electrostatic charge in the surrounding space, just as a magnet produces a permanent magnetic field. And like a magnet, it can be used to build a motor.

Jefimenko chose the electrostatic motor for his project because the earth-field antennas develop extremely high-voltage low-current power -- and unlike the electromagnetic motor -- that's exactly what it needs.

The Climactic Experiment

On the night of Sept. 29, 1970, Jefimenko and Walker strolled into an empty parking lot, and hiked a 24-foot pole painted day-glow orange into the sky. On the pole's end was a bit of radioactive material in a capsule connected to a wire. The experimenters hooked an electret motor to the antenna, and, as Jefimenko describes it, "the energy of the earth's electrical field was converted into continuous mechanical motion."

Two months later, they successfully operated operated a corona motor from electricity in the air.

Any Future in It?

Whether the earth's electrical field will ever be an important source of power is open to question. There are millions -- perhaps billions -- of kilowatts of electrical energy flowing into the earth constantly. Jefimenko thinks that earth-field antennas could be built to extract viable amounts of it.

But whether or not we tap this energy source, the electrostatic motor could become important on its own.

- In space or aviation, its extreme light weight could be crucial. Jefimenko estimates that corona motors could deliver one horsepower for each 3 pounds of weight.
- They'd be valuable in laboratories where even the weakest magnetic field could upset an experiment.
- Suspended on air bearings, they'd make good gyroscopes.

In a particularly spectacular experiment, Jefimenko turned on a Van de Graaff generator -- a device that creates a very-high-voltage field. About a yard away he placed a sharp-pointed corona antenna and connected it to an electrostatic motor. The rotor began to spin. The current was flowing from the generator through the air to where it was being picked up by the antenna.

The stunt had a serious purpose: The earth's field is greatest on mountaintops. Jefimenko would like to set up a large antenna in such a spot, then aim an ultraviolet laser beam at a receiving site miles away at ground level. The laser beam would ionize the air, creating an invisible conductor through apparently empty space.

To be sure, many difficulties exist; and no one knows for sure whether we'll ever get useful amounts of power out of the air. But with thinking like that, Jefimenko's a hard man to ignore.

Reprint of *Popular Science* Article (May 1971)

Electrostatic Motors You Can Build

By C.P. Gilmore & William J. Hawkins

When we crank up the electrostatic motor at the end of this article, people always want to know what makes it run. It is mysterious -- there's nothing but a plastic disk and two strange electrodes. Yet there it is, spinning merrily.

In "The Amazing Motor That Draws Power From the Air", last month, we told about our visit to the laboratory of Dr. Oleg Jefimenko at the University of West Virginia, who has designed and built a variety of these ingenious machines. now, as promised, we bring you details on how you can build your own electrostatic motor from simple materials.

The devices that you see here are corona-discharge motors. The sharp-pointed or knife-edge electrodes create a corona, which ionizes or charges the air particles floating by. These charged particles transfer their charge to the closest part of the plastic rotor and charge it up, just as you can charge your body by walking across a wool rug on a dry winter's day.

Once a spot on the rotor assumes a charge, it is repelled from the chargin electrode by electrostatic forces, and at the same time is attracted to the other electrode, which has an opposite charge. When the charged section of the rotor reaches the opposite electrode, another corona discharge reverses the polarity and starts the whole thing over again.

The Concept is Simple

And so are the motors. But that doesn't mean they're easy to build. These motors run on millionths of a watt; they've got no power to waste turning stiff bearings or slightly misaligned rotors. So they must be built with watch-making precision.

They're made of acrylic sheet, rod, and tube stock -- Plexiglas and Lucite are two of the better-known brands. Acrylic cuts and works beautifully. Cut edges can be sanded so they have a white, frosted appearance that, in contrast with clear surfaces, gives your finished motor a sparkling, jewel-like appearance. If you like clear edges, you can buff them on a wheel and the whole thing becomes transparent.

Drill and tap the acrylic and assemble parts with machine screws. This allows for fine adjustment and alignment. Later, you can make the whole thing permanent by putting a little solvent along the joints. The solvent flows into the joint and fuses it permanently.

Details of framework, support and so on aren't important; change them if you like. but work with care if you want to avoid headaches. The Poggendorff motor looked simple; we slapped it together in a couple of hours, hooked up the power source -- and nothing happened. We gave it a few helpful spins by hand, but it wouldn't keep running.

The cure took about 3 hours. First, we noticed that the outer edge of the disk wobbled from side to side about 1/16 of an inch as the wheel revolved. So the rotor-electrode distance was constantly changing. There was a little play in the 1/4" hole we had drilled for the electrodes -- so they weren't lined up absolutely square with the disk. Then we noticed that the disk always stopped with one side down. The imbalance was only a fraction of an ounce -- but it was too much.

We drilled out the old hub and cemented in a new one -- this time, carefully. We lined up the electrodes -- precisely. Then, once more spinning the disk by hand, we added bit of masking tape until it was perfectly balanced. We connected the power -- and slowly... slowly... the disk began to turn. After about a minute, we clocked some turns with a watch and found it was spinning at 200 rpm. A moment later, we lost count. It was a great feeling.

Where Tolerances Are Brutal

We had even more trouble with the octagonal-window machine. When it wouldn't run and we turned the shaft by hand, we could feel the rotor dragging. We took it apart, felt all the surfaces on the rotor and the framework's insides and found a few bits of hardened cement, which we removed. We filed down all edges on the rotor and the windows to make sure there were no beads or chips dragging.

The rotor and corner separators are made from the same sheet of 1/2" plastic, so rotor clearance is achieved by putting shims at the corners to hold the side plates slightly more than 1/2" apart. With the 1/16" shims we were using, we could see that the sides were slightly misaligned so the shaft was not being held at a true 90 degrees. We drilled slightly oversized holes in the corners of one side piece and carefully adjusted until the rotor was turning true in the slot. To give the motor more torque, we put a bead of cement along the outer edge of each aluminum-foil electrode to stop corona leakage. The motor ran.

Take a Giant Step

Once you've built these machines, why not design your own? Start with the Jefimenko 1/10 hp model (pictured) as a challenge. Then plan one from scratch. You can power your motors with a laboratory high-voltage supply, a Van de Graff generator, or a Wimhurst machine or any other high-voltage source. We've been running ours on the home-built Wimhurst machine shown in the photos. (If you don't want to build one, Wimhurst machines are available from scientific supply houses such as Edmund Scientific).

The discharge globes are traditional for high-voltage machines. They aren't necessary, but they give a quick check on machine operation and a satisfying arc when you move them within 1/2" of each other. Incidentally, that funny smell is ozone. But its concentration is too low to be harmful. The generator is safe, too. You can hold both electrodes in your hands and all you'll feel is a tingle. This particular generator, we estimate, puts out about 30,000 volts.

To make wiring simple, we used standard connectors on the Wimhurst collectors, and meter leads with regular banana plugs and alligator clips to hook up the motors.

Last month, we mentioned seeing Dr Jefimenko run his electrostatic motors on electricity tapped from the earth's field. We haven't had a chance to try this yet with ours, but it should work. If you want to try, you'll need a needle-pointed piece of music wire a few inches long to start a corona, plus several hundred feet of fine copper wire.

Connect the pointed wire to the fine conductor, get the sharp point up into the air at least 200-300 feet with a kite or balloon, and hook the wire to one side of the motor. Hook the other side of the motor to ground. The earth field antenna should at times be able to develop up to 20,000 volts from the earth's electrical field. If nothing happens, check your equipment, or try another day. The field changes constantly.

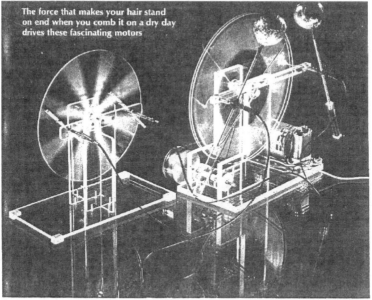

The force that makes your hair stand on end when you comb it on a dry day drives these fascinating motors

The electrostatic motor on the left turns between three- and four-hundred rpm when connected to the Wimshurst generator at right.

This octagonal-window design makes motor handsome, self-starting

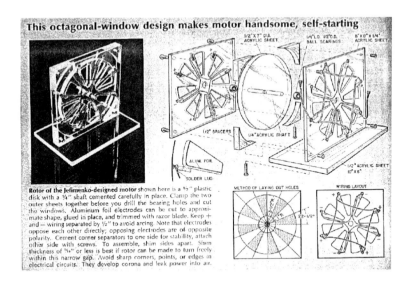

Rotor of the Jefimenko-designed motor shown here is a ½" plastic disk with a ¼" shaft cemented carefully in place. Clamp the two outer sheets together before you drill the bearing holes and cut the windows. Aluminum foil electrodes can be cut to approximate shape, glued in place, and trimmed with razor blade. Keep + and — wiring separated by ½" to avoid arcing. Note that electrodes oppose each other directly; opposing electrodes are of opposite polarity. Cement corner separators to one side for stability, attach other side with screws. To assemble, shim sides apart. Shim thickness of ¹⁄₁₆" or less is best if rotor can be made to turn freely within this narrow gap. Avoid sharp corners, points, or edges in electrical circuits. They develop corona and leak power into air.

Wimshurst machine generates 30,000 volts

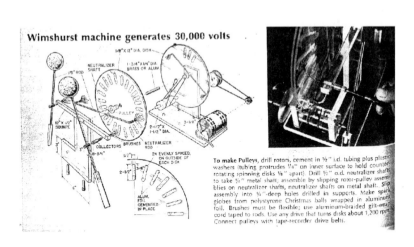

To make Pulleys, drill rotors, cement in ½" i.d. tubing plus plastic washers (tubing protrudes ¼" on inner surface to hold counterrotating spinning disks ⅛" apart). Drill ½" o.d. neutralizer shafts to take ¼" metal shaft; assemble by slipping rotor-pulley assemblies on neutralizer shafts, neutralizer shafts on metal shaft. Slip assembly into ¼"-deep holes drilled in supports. Make spark globes from polystyrene Christmas balls wrapped in aluminum foil. Brushes must be flexible; use aluminum-braided gift-wrap cord taped to rods. Use any drive that turns disks about 1,200 rpm. Connect pulleys with tape-recorder drive belts.

142

Best first project: motor designed by physicist J. C. Poggendorff in 1870

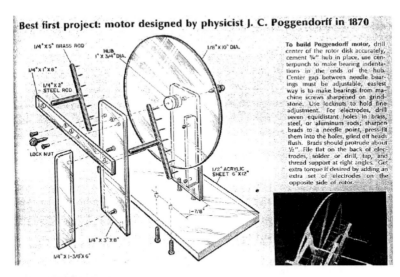

1/4" X 5" BRASS ROD
HUB 1" X 3/4" DIA.
1/8" X 10" DIA.
1/4" X 1" X 8"
1/4" X 2" STEEL ROD
LOCK NUT
1/2" ACRYLIC SHEET 6" X 12"
1-7/8"
1/4" X 3" X 8"
1/4" X 1-3/8" X 6"

To build Poggendorff motor, drill center of the rotor disk accurately, cement ¾" hub in place, use centerpunch to make bearing indentations in the ends of the hub. Center gap between needle bearings must be adjustable, easiest way is to make bearings from machine screws sharpened on grindstone. Use locknuts to hold fine adjustment. For electrodes, drill seven equidistant holes in brass, steel, or aluminum rods; sharpen brads to a needle point, press-fit them into the holes, grind off heads flush. Brads should protrude about ½". File flat on the back of electrodes, solder or drill, tap, and thread support at right angles. Get extra torque if desired by adding an extra set of electrodes on the opposite side of rotor.

Mounting, with rotor removed, shows the relative positions of supports, needle bearings, and electrodes. Electrode points should be close to disk, but not touching.

Note: p. 144 has been removed .

See US patents 5,965,968 and 5,015,906 for recent, practical electrostatic motors, from www.google.com/patents - Ed. Note

Department of Physics

West Virginia University

Eberly College of Arts and Sciences

May 3, 1999

Mr. Thomas Valone, President
Integrity Research Institute
1422 K Street NW, Suite 204
Washington, D. C. 20005

Dear Mr. Valone:

Thank you for inviting me to submit a paper for *Proceedings of COFE.* Enclosed please find my paper "Electrostatic Energy Resources, Electrostatic Generators, and Electrostatic Motors." I hope the paper meets whith your requirements.

Sincerely yours,

Oleg D. Jefimenko
Preofessor of Physics

304-293-3422 · FAX 304-293-5732 · PO Box 6315 · Morgantown WV 26506-6315
Equal Opportunity / Affirmative Action Institution

ELECTROSTATIC ENERGY RESOURCES, ELECTROSTATIC GENERATORS, AND ELECTROSTATIC MOTORS

Oleg D. Jefimenko

Department of Physics, West Virginia University

P. O. Box 6315

Morgantown, W.V. 26506-6315

Abstract

Utilization and conversion of electrostatic energy is still an essentially unexplored area of physics and engineering, although there are compelling reasons to believe that such utilization and conversion will be of considerable significance in the future. This paper presents a brief discussion of the following three subjects associated with electrostatic energy and its utilization: (a) the earth's electric field as a natural source of electrostatic energy, (b) generation of electrostatic energy, and (c) conversion and utilization of electrostatic energy by means of electrostatic motors.

1. Introduction

The science of electrostatics was first developed in the 18th century at a time when the technology and industry were not yet sufficiently advanced to put it to practical uses. As a result, serious research in electrostatics soon lost its momentum and, except for a few isolated efforts, was practically nonexistent during the entire 19th century. Spectacular advances in

1

electromagnetics during the second half of the 19th century and the first half of the 20th century, upon which our present-day technology is essentially based, contributed even more to the neglect of electrostatics as a science and as a branch of electrical engineering. Only recently practical aspects of electrostatics began to make noticeable impact on the industry and economy, and the once forgotten science has again appeared at the focal point of serious scientific investigations. An important branch of these investigations is the study of methods and techniques for utilization, generation, and conversion of electrostatic energy. A brief survey of the results of such studies is presented in this paper. Specifically, the following three subjects will be discussed: (a) the earth's electric field as a natural source of electrostatic energy, (b) generation of electrostatic energy, and (c) conversion of electrostatic energy by means of electrostatic motors.

2. The Earth's Electric Field

Our planet is a huge generator of electricity supplying the atmosphere near the earth's surface with an apparently inexhaustible surplus of positive electric charges. The awesome manifestation of atmospheric electricity as lightning and thunder is known to everyone. What is less known is that atmospheric electricity is always with us, and that the lightning is merely a fuse which "blows" whenever too much electric charge accumulates in the air and in the clouds.

The invisible layer of positive electric charges in the atmosphere is about 20 km thick. The concentration of the charges is greatest at the earth's surface and diminishes with altitude rather rapidly.

2

The electric field produced by these charges varies from place to place and changes with atmospheric conditions. Near the ground the fair-weather electric field is, on an average, 120 volts/m. This means that if one erects a 10 m high "earth-field" antenna, one obtains a voltage of 1,200 volts between the tip of the antenna and the ground. Correspondingly larger voltages can be obtained from higher antennas, although for very high antennas the voltage increases by less than 120 volts per meter. During electric storms the atmospheric electric field may increase to 3×10^5 volts/m. An antenna 10 m high would then produce a voltage of 3,000,000 volts between the tip and the ground.

The minimum fair-weather energy density of the atmospheric electric field at the surface of the earth is on an average 10^{-7} joules/m^3. Assuming that this energy density extends to a height of 1 km, one obtains 10^{-4} joules for the energy contained in the fair-weather atmospheric electric field above each m^2 of the earth's surface. The maximum energy density occurs during electric storms and is about 1 joule/m^3. This corresponds to approximately 1,000 joules for each m^2 of the earth's surface beneath the storms.

The atmosphere is not a perfect insulator, and therefore there is an electric leakage current between the atmosphere and the earth that tends to dissipate the atmospheric electric charges and thus to destroy the atmospheric electric field. The fair-weather density of this current is of the order 10^{-12} amp/m^2 corresponding to energy dissipation of about 10^{-10} joules/m$^3 \cdot$ sec. The rate of energy dissipation per m^2 of the earth's surface (assuming, as before, that the field extends to only 1 km above the ground) is therefore 10^{-7} watts/m^2. It is important to note that the leakage current would destroy the atmospheric electric field in less than 1 hour if the electric charges of the atmosphere were not maintained by other processes.

3

The maximum electric current between the atmosphere and the earth occurs during electric storms and is about 10^{-8} amp/m^2 (this is the average current and is not to be confused with the current of a lightning bolt, which is of the order of 10^4 amp and dissipates approximately 100 kilowatt-hours of energy). Assuming that the electric field during electric storms is 10^5 volts/m, one finds that in stormy weather the dissipation of atmospheric electric field energy is 10^{-3} joules/m$^3\cdot$sec. The rate of energy dissipation per m^2 of the earth's surface is therefore about 1 watt/m (beneath the storms).

Taking into account that at any given time there are nearly 2,000 electric storms around the globe and that each storm occupies an area of about 10^8 m^2, one finds that the overall dissipation of the atmospheric electric field energy occurs at the rate of 2×10^{11} watts. Consequently, the electric power potentially obtainable from the atmospheric electric field for the entire earth is not less than 200,000 megawatts. It should be noted that in arriving at this figure we have not used the figures for the energy content of the atmospheric electric field. This is because the energy content as such has no bearing on the power obtainable from the field. The power depends only on *how fast* the energy can be extracted from the field and *how fast* the field can replenish itself.

The recognition of the fact that the atmospheric electric field constitutes an energy source dates back to Benjamin Franklin, who constructed electric chimes powered by a sharp point antenna. H. C. Vion, in 1860, proposed to collect atmospheric electricity by means of an antenna formed by a network of wires.[1] Several years later, Mahlon Loomis suggested for this purpose an antenna consisting of several concentric metal rings supporting numerous metallic brushes.[2] M. W. Dewey, in 1889, depicted an antenna in the shape of a crown studded with

4

numerous sharp spikes.[3] None of these inventors reported any actual testing or operation of their antennas.

Experiments performed several years ago in the authors laboratory brought the idea of utilizing the energy of the atmospheric electric field closer to fulfillment. Two electrostatic motors (see Section 4) of novel design were operated by atmospheric electricity with the help of a sharp-point earth-field antenna and an radioactive earth-field antenna.[4] Although the power obtainable from these antennas was only about 10^{-3} watts, the experiments have proved that it is entirely possible to extract and to use the energy of the atmospheric electric field, the fair-weather field in particular.

The significance of the atmospheric electric field as an energy source is frequently downrated by regarding it as a depletable energy source. The fact is however that this field replenishes itself by natural processes, so that the power obtainable from it is limited only by the rate at which it is capable of restoring itself. Consequently, one is well justified to explore the possibility of developing a technology for extracting energy from this reservoir. The two most important steps that should be made in this direction are to develop efficient energy-extracting antennas and to develop devices capable of utilizing the energy provided by the antennas.

Two types of antennas have been used thus far: the sharp-point antenna and the radioactive antenna.

A sharp-point antenna consists of an insulating mast at the top of which there is a sharp metallic point. This antenna depends for its operation on a corona discharge from the sharp point that takes place when the sharp point is placed at a height where the potential is 6,000 volts or

5

more relative to the ground. The antenna does not work unless this "threshold" voltage is reached, and this is its main disadvantage. The fair-weather current obtainable from such an antenna is of the order of 10^6 amp.

A radioactive antenna consists of an insulating mast carrying on its top a quantity of radioactive material (an α- or β-source). There is no threshold voltage for its operation, and it can work at any height above the ground. The current that such an antenna produces essentially depends on the activity of the radioactive material used in it. Also radioactive antennas have not yet been sufficiently studied for any recommendations on their usefulness or practicality.

A characteristic property of earth-field antennas is that they have inherently very large resistance and produce relatively high voltages. Thus only a device requiring for its operation a high voltage and a low current, or an "extra high impedance" device, can be successfully operated by these antennas. Calculations have shown that the needed impedance is at least 10^5 ohms. An impedance of this magnitude is not practical with usual electromagnetic motors or other devices whose very nature demands the use of low voltages and relatively high currents. But even much higher impedances are attainable with electrostatic motors and other electrostatic devices. This is why an earth-field antenna can power, for instance, an electrostatic motor but is absolutely useless for operating an ordinary electromagnetic motor or for lighting an incandescent bulb.

It is not yet clear whether sharp-point or radioactive antennas can ever be developed to the extent that they will achieve practical significance. It is more likely that if the energy of the atmospheric (or ionospheric) electric field will ever be put to practical uses, it will be done by yet unknown means. Among the different possibilities are laser beams and charged particle

6

beams capable of conducting electric current. Such beams could conceivably be used not only as earth-field antennas, but also as a means for following and discharging electrified clouds and even for extracting energy from the ionosphere, whose energy content is much higher than that of the atmospheric electric field.

Naturally, we do not know whether or not atmospheric (or ionospheric) electricity will ever be useful to mankind as an energy source. But, as it is clear from the above discussion, we have good reasons to believe that it might be. Clearly, therefore, further explorations of this possibility will directly or indirectly contribute to the quest for new sources of energy and for the more efficient utilization or conversion of the presently available resources.

3. Electrostatic Generators

There hardly is any process or activity, natural or manmade, which is not accompanied by generation of "static" electricity. One of the simplest of such processes is the placing two different bodies in close contact and then separating them. After the two bodies are separated, each shows a charge of opposite polarity. An especially close contact is produced by friction, and on this principle the so-called "electrostatic friction machines" (generators) were first built some 300 years ago. In the 19th century the more efficient "induction", or "influence", machines were developed. Although more complex than the friction machines, they likewise were simple to construct and to operate.[5] This simplicity of construction and design is an important characteristics of electrostatic generators.

Electric current in electrostatic generators is produced by a mechanical transport of charges (convection current). In generators where charges are carried on rotating disks,

7

cylinders, or belts the transport velocity, and hence the output power, is limited by the mechanical strength of the transporting system. The presently attainable maximum output of such generators is exemplified by a 10 kilowatts machine with a 40-cm diameter disk rotating at 24,000 rpm. Higher transport velocities can be attained by transporting charges by means of streaming fluids or gases. The output power achieved with such generators is about 1 kilowatt.

Both the output power and the output voltage can be increased by embedding electrostatic generators in liquids of high permittivity and break-down strength. Generators of this type have been built for an output power of up to 1 kilowatt.[6]

Novel types of low-power electrostatic generators with electrets (permanently charged dielectrics) as active elements were designed and tested several years ago in the author's laboratory.[7,8]

Electrostatic generators are presently economical where dc voltages in excess of 100 kilovolts and currents of up to 10^2 amp are required (corresponding to an output power of about 10 kilowatts or less). Outside this range they are usually inferior to electromagnetic generators or generator-transformer-rectifier assemblies. An important exception is space applications and portable equipment, where the low weight and/or absence of magnetic fields are essential. Furthermore, because of their high output impedance, electrostatic generators are ideally suited to supply power to electrostatic motors, and together with such motors may form in the future highly efficient low-cost energy converting systems.

4. Electrostatic Motors

Conventional electric motors, or electromagnetic motors, create mechanical motion as

8

153

a result of magnetic forces acting upon electric currents. *Electrostatic motors* create the motion as a result of electric, or "electrostatic", forces acting between electric charges. It is important to note that in the nature the electrostatic forces are much stronger than the magnetic ones. Thus, for example, although a considerable effort may be needed to separate a magnet from an object attracted by it, a much greater effort is needed to break the magnet; this is because the magnet holds the object by magnetic forces, while the molecules of matter in the magnet (as well as in any other body) are held together by electrostatic forces.

Although electrostatic motors are not yet widely known or used, they already hold at least five records as compared with the electromagnetic motors:

1. The first electric motor ever invented was electrostatic. It was built about 100 years before the first electromagnetic motor was conceived.

2. The electric motor that operated without interruption longer than any other motor was electrostatic. It was installed at the University of Insbruck, Austria, in 1823 and operated continuously at least until 1909 powered by a Zamboni pile (an early high-voltage battery).

3. Electrostatic motors have been operated from voltages in excess of 10^5 volts.

4. Electrostatic motors have been operated by using currents smaller than 10^{-9} amp.

5. The first electric motor that operated directly from atmospheric electricity was electrostatic.

Many different types and designs of electrostatic motors are possible.[9,10,11,12] It is customary to classify electrostatic motors in accordance with their mode of operation or design. Thus, depending on how electric charges are delivered to the active part of a motor one speaks of *contact motors*, *spark motors*, *induction motors*, and *electret motors*. In reference to the

9

154

medium in which the active part of a motor is located one speaks of *liquid-* or *gas-immersed motors*. In reference to the material and design of the active part of a motor one speaks of *dielectric motors* and *capacitor motors*. Finally, in reference to the rate of rotation of a motor relative to the period of the applied voltage one speaks of *synchronous motors, asynchronous motors,* and *pulsed motors.*

The most powerful electrostatic motors reported to this day are corona motors. In these motors charges are sprayed onto the rotor by a corona discharge from stator electrodes. The rotor may be a cylinder or a disk. A disk rotor and stator can be made in the form of a thin "sandwich", and many such "sandwiches" can be placed on a single axle thus forming a compound motor in which very good use is made of the entire volume occupied by the motor. Such motors can be made more compact and considerably lighter than electromagnetic motors of the same power output. It is expected that a motor 1 m on a side will provide a power of about 1 megawatt and will weigh 500 kg or less.

Corona motors require for their operation a voltage from several thousand volts (for air-filled motors), to several hundred volts (for gas-filled motors). This is because a certain threshold voltage is needed to initiate a corona discharge between the stator and the rotor. There are, however, other types of electrostatic motors (electret motors, for example) that can be operated from as low a voltage as one may wish.

Electrostatic motors possess a number of unique properties. One of them is that electrostatic motors require very little metal for their construction. The bulk of such a motor can be made of plastic or other similar materials. Therefore these motors have very high ratio of output power to weight. They are inexpensive and easy to build, and, what is most important,

10

155

they can operate from a much greater variety of sources than the conventional electromagnetic motors. Any source used for operating conventional electromagnetic motors can be used to operate electrostatic motors. However, electrostatic motors can operate also from sources from which no other motors can operate. Therefore, by using electrostatic motors, one may achieve a much better utilization of the available energy sources and a more efficient transformation of available energy. Among the many unusual sources that can be used to operate electrostatic motors are: charged capacitors, high-impedance chemical batteries, electrostatic generators, nuclear batteries, and atmospheric electricity.

In conclusion it should be pointed out that almost all papers on electrostatic motors published thus far deal with qualitative aspects of the performance of the various types of motors. Only very few papers deal with the theory of operation, optimization of design, and with quantitative aspects of the operation of the motors. It is clear therefore that electrostatic motors still constitute an essentially unexplored area of physics and engineering, and that electrostatic motor research must be considered as a potentially highly rewarding area among the many energy-related research endeavors.

References

1.   H. C. Vion, "Improved Method of Utilizing Atmospheric Electricity," U.S. Patent No. 28793 (June 19, 1860).

2.   See T. Appleby, *Mahlon Loomis. Inventor of Radio* (Loomis Publications, Washington, 1967) p. 123.

11

156

3.   M. W. Dewey, "Method of Utilizing Natural Electric Energy," U. S. Patent No. 414943 (November 12, 1889).

4.   O. D. Jefimenko, "Operation of electric motors from atmospheric electric field," Am. J. Phys. **39**, 776-779 (1971).

5.   See, for example, A. Steinbach and R. A. Ford, "The Electrostatic Machines of Holtz and Wimshurst," Electric Spacecraft Journal, Issue **15**, 27-36 (1995).

6.   For references on modern electrostatic generators see M. J. Mulcahy and W. R. Bell, "Electrostatic Generators" in *Electrostatics and its Applications*, A. D. Moore, Ed., (Wiley, New York, 1973) pp. 148-179.

7.   O. D. Jefimenko and N. Y. Sun, "Spherical Carnauba Wax Electrets", In *Electrets, Charge Storage, and Transport in Dielectrics*, The Electrochemical Society, New York, 1973, pp. 462-573.

8.   O. D. Jefimenko and D. K. Walker, "Electrostatic Current-Generator Having a Disk Electret as Active Element," IEEE Trans. Ind. Appl. **IA-14**, 537-538 (1978).

9.   O. D. Jefimenko, *Electrostatic Motors: Their History, Types, and Principles of Operation*, (Electret Scientific, Star City, West Virginia, 1973).

10.   O. D. Jefimenko, "Electrostatic Motors" in *Electrostatics and its Applications* A. D. Moore, Ed., (Wiley, New York, 1973) pp. 131-147.

11.   O. D. Jefimenko and D. K. Walker, "Electrostatic Motors," The Physics Teacher, **9**, 121- 129 (1971).

12. See also "Electric Propulsion Patents 1928-1995," Electric Spacecraft Journal, Issue **19**, 16- 27 (1996).

12

157

INDEX